MIRANDIZED NATION:
The Inside Story of Ernesto Miranda and the Phoenix Police Department

TIMOTHY W. MOORE
and
CLARK LOHR

Be Safe!
Timothy W. Moore

Happy Reading!
Clark Lohr

Published by
Phoenix Sleuth, LLC

Phoenix Sleuth, LLC

Copyright Information

MIRANDIZED NATION: The Inside Story of Ernesto Miranda

Portions of this book are fictionalized.

Cover Design and Layout: Kästle Olson
Interior Design and Formatting: Deborah J Ledford

ISBN: 978-0-692-43281-5

Manufactured in the United States of America

DEDICATION

This book is dedicated to the men and women
of law enforcement, past, present, and future.

AUTHOR'S STATEMENT

Most people in the United States understand the Miranda Decision requires the police to advise suspects of certain constitutional rights before interrogating them.

As of now the Miranda Warnings are only required to be given under certain circumstances. One is if the suspect is in custody and two is if the officer/detective is going to ask specific questions about a specific crime. Miranda Warnings do not apply and are not required unless both of these circumstances are present.

The Miranda Decision of 1966 is approaching its fiftieth birthday in 2016. The authors believe the Miranda Warnings by and large have benefited both the public and the police.

The Miranda Decision has helped to safeguard the rights of individuals in the communities officers are sworn to protect and it has made police departments more professional by becoming a standard used by the men and women in law enforcement every day across this Mirandized Nation.

MIRANDIZED NATION: The Inside Story of Ernesto Miranda and the Phoenix Police Department tells the story of the Phoenix PD investigation that ended in Ernest Miranda's arrest, revealing how law enforcement operated before, during, and after the Miranda Ruling by the United States Supreme Court.

In order to form the core of this book we relied as much as possible on primary sources: interviews with retired officers and detectives, including the arresting officer, Carroll Cooley, as well as newspaper articles, government documents, and Miranda's family members. Some of the dialog and the characterization of the players have been fictionalized to facilitate the story. The names of some individuals, including victims and witnesses, have been changed. Nothing else on these pages are invented.

A portion of the proceeds from this book will be donated to the Fraternal Order of Police, the Phoenix Police Museum, and the Phoenix Law Enforcement Association.

Timothy W. Moore

INTRODUCTION

In the late 1950s and early 1960s a Mesa resident Ernest A. Miranda, started his life of crime that ultimately led to his violent death. This book is part fiction but is based on the facts of the actual case involving Miranda's life, and the individuals who were his victims as well as his legal pursuers. Ernest Miranda was a pathetic individual who preyed on the innocent and was ultimately arrested for the kidnapping, assault, rape and robbery of an eighteen year old female. He was also charged with similar crimes against other female victims in 1959, 1962 and early 1963.

Miranda vs Arizona, 384 U.S. 436 (1966), changed the way police officers interrogated suspects at the time of arrest. The individuals involved in the arrest and conviction of Ernest Miranda followed the Rules of Law in place at the time of his arrest. The U.S. Supreme Court, by instituting the Miranda decision changed the Rules of Law or procedures that police officers were to follow during the arrest and interrogation of criminal suspects.

This story introduces facts that led up to the Miranda decision and what happened as a result of that formal judgment. The story of Ernest A. Miranda's life ultimately ends with his violent death in a barroom fight. Many would say "Justice was Served…"

Dennis A. Garret
Phoenix Police Chief (retired)

FORWARD

Those who work in law enforcement have chosen a career that is rewarding and provides a sense of accomplishment and service to one's community. However, with that said, being a police officer is never easy. Law enforcement is extremely dangerous and the demands and stress to police officers and their families are extraordinary.

One of the most difficult parts of their job is the requirement that police officers stay abreast of our criminal laws and the procedural requirements of our Courts. Legislation and court decisions are constantly evolving all aspects of law enforcement. Law enforcement is extremely complicated and every police officer knows that if they make one mistake, a dangerous criminal can go free; perhaps to further victimize.

Every so often a major court decision is issued that dramatically changes our criminal justice system. *Miranda vs Arizona* is such a case. This 1966, precedent setting case dramatically changed law enforcement for each police officer in the country. Now, every officer is required to comply with the United States Supreme Court's decision which mandates that prior to interviewing a suspect who is "under custodial arrest", the suspect must be read their "Miranda Rights". If the police officer fails to do so, the suspects' statements and confession are suppressed and cannot be used at trial.

It is critical that we accurately record the history and background of this precedent setting case. *Mirandized Nation: The Inside Story of Ernesto Miranda and the Phoenix Police Department* is an excellent account and provides a fascinating inside look of one of the most important cases in law enforcement history.

Richard M. Romley
Maricopa County Attorney
1989-2004
Interim 2010

ONE

ON THE EVENING of March 2, 1963, Ernesto "Ernie" Miranda got into his faded, white-over-gray 1953 Packard and backed out of his driveway in the 200 block of North Le Baron Street in Mesa, Arizona. He turned down a side street, then headed north on Country Club Drive. The temperature approached sixty degrees, an escape from the eighty degrees it had been during the day. Ernie's old Packard looked light green under the street lamps.

Ernie took a drag from the cigarette dangling from his lips. He wasn't going to work like he'd told Twila, his common-law wife. She remained at home with their infant daughter, along with two of her children from a previous relationship.

Just after 8:00 p.m. Ernie bought a six-pack of beer and a pack of cigarettes at the Circle K convenience store at 6th Street and Country Club. He rummaged around in the glove box of his Packard and found a four-inch metal bottle opener. He grabbed a sweating bottle of beer from the sack, leveraged off the cap, and took a swig. Then he lit another cigarette off the butt of the first one. He left Mesa a few minutes later.

The twenty-mile drive into Phoenix gave him time to think. Ernie took a drag from his cigarette. "I'll have to do it better this time," he said, exhaling a lungful of smoke toward the windshield. He emptied the beer bottle with a long pull and tossed it onto the

1

passenger-side floor. *The beer can only help.* He reached into the sack and opened another bottle.

Thirty minutes later he arrived in downtown Phoenix where, except for the streetlights, it was nice and dark. Ernie watched for women walking alone and for those who rode public transport. He followed a bus for a few stops and watched the girls get off in pairs. He was disappointed, he continued on.

He eventually spotted a bus going north on 7th Street, leaving the downtown area. He followed it and saw the stops on the main streets were well lit and the streets in between were much darker. A plan started to take shape in his mind.

Ernie turned the Packard east onto Bethany Home Road and drove into the desert out near the Biltmore at 24th street. The less populated area had roads that led to remote places. He scouted a side street that would work into his plan. He marked it in his mind. *If all goes well I'll be back soon.*

It was closing in on 11:00 p.m. when he pulled into the downtown area of Phoenix. Ernie turned right onto Adams, past the Paramount Theatre at 2nd Avenue. There, Ernie saw a young woman who worked in the theater. She was walking to her bus stop. He'd watched her before and knew she got off the bus at Marlette. Ernie drove ahead of the bus. He would be waiting for her.

AT 11:15 P.M., eighteen-year-old Margaret Fair, known to her friends and family as Maggie, completed her shift and left the Paramount Theatre. It was Saturday night. She didn't have a date like some of the other girls, so she didn't mind working. Maggie liked the Paramount and its history. During her breaks she would take walks backstage and in the basement of the theater, where only actors and stagehands had access when the facility presented live performances. She would look dreamily at the old movie posters that adorned the walls. She thought the plays and movies were romantic. The actors had outgoing personalities and lives filled with endless adventures and happy endings. Quite a contrast to Maggie's shy, introverted personality and much simpler life.

Maggie stepped out of the theater. She stood in the crisp night air and looked at the bright theater marquee. She watched the way the lights appeared to move when they came on and off, framing the white background with bold black letters that read: *The Longest Day*. It was the latest movie playing for the week.

Maggie walked two blocks east to the bus stop with coworker Reginald Fertig. She liked riding the bus with someone she knew and, although he was twenty-one years old, he had never made a pass at her and the two of them had never dated.

The air brakes hissed as the bus came to a stop. The folding doors opened and, as they had done many times before, they boarded at 11:45 p.m. They sat down together in a forward facing seat near the front of the bus. The bus rumbled away from the curb.

ERNIE SAT IN his car, smoking a cigarette. He had parked in the shadows behind a ballet school located in a strip mall on the northeast corner of 7th Street and Marlette Avenue. He finished the last beer from his six-pack and went over the plan in his mind. It was nearly midnight and the city bus would soon arrive.

He took a drag from his cigarette as he cut a quarter-inch-thick hemp rope into a manageable length. He fidgeted and fondled his knife. He'd manipulated the knife so often he could flick the blade open using only the thumb of one hand.

He stared at the darkened windows of the ballet school. Had this been earlier in the evening class would still be in session. Ernie envisioned the girls practicing in their tutus. Thin-layered cloth would flow over their tights and leggings. The bright colored fabric would rise and fall as the girls danced.

The students couldn't see out through the front glass windows when the inside lights were on and no one could tell if anyone was watching the girls from the other side of the glass windows.

SHORTLY AFTER MIDNIGHT the northbound city bus ground to a stop at Marlette Avenue. The air brakes hissed. The doors accordioned open. *Right on time*, Ernie thought. Margaret Fair stepped off the bus and waved back at Reginald Fertig and the bus driver. She walked east on Marlette. She was five blocks away from where she lived. She could be home by 12:20.

Suddenly, an engine roared and tires squealed. Maggie turned and headlights blinded her. She clutched her purse and jumped back as the vehicle nearly struck her. She moved quickly and kept from falling as the car drove east on Marlette. Maggie's hand went to her chest and she caught her breath, realizing she had nearly been run down. She held her arms out, holding her purse in one hand, and looked herself over. She was startled but uninjured.

The car disappeared into the darkness. *That was strange.* She continued to walk down Marlette, away from the corner businesses and into the neighborhood. She tried to think if she knew anyone who drove an older, light-green sedan.

After driving a city block down Marlette, Ernie turned off the car lights and rolled to a stop at the north curb in front of a vacant lot. The neighborhood was not fully built up and there were no sidewalks or streetlights on Marlette. Trees in the yards, though sparse of leaves, blocked some of the light given off by the first-quarter moon. Ernie took deep breaths, rocked forward and back in the front seat, and tried to regain his composure. *I almost ran her over.*

Ernie thought back on his previous adventures of this type. He had begun by watching girls and women through their bedroom windows. *Surely they would draw the drapes if they didn't want me to watch them undress for bed.* One woman was so inviting, he had entered the house and gotten into bed with her. *If her husband didn't come home, I could have had my way with her.* Ernie rubbed his palms together and grinned. He went over his new plan and waited in the car, in the darkness.

MAGGIE FAIR CONTINUED walking in the street close to the north curb on Marlette. A block down the road she came upon a dirty, light-green car parked across from an apartment building. She didn't see a driver and assumed the car had been there for some time. *Could it be the same car? They all look so much alike these days.*

Maggie kept walking past the passenger side of the car. A man jumped out of the driver-side door and came around the front of the vehicle. Maggie tried to run. He grabbed her by the arm and forced it behind her back. She let go of her purse so he might take it and run away. Then a click sounded and the point of a knife was at her throat. She started to scream. The man let go of her arm and quickly covered her mouth with his hand. He pulled her head back. She felt his glasses rub against her head above her right ear.

"Don't scream. Don't scream and you won't get hurt."

Maggie nodded her head. She hoped the man wouldn't hurt her. Maggie was too afraid to try to escape. She trembled. Tears streaked down her cheeks and onto Ernie's hand. She thought she was going to die.

"Get into the back seat and lay down on your stomach."

Maggie saw no one on the darkened street that she could call to for help. Ernie opened the passenger-side back door, kept his hand on her mouth, and forced her into the vehicle. She saw no one else in the car and she reluctantly lay down. Maggie wanted to believe if she did what the man said he wouldn't hurt her. Her sister had told her if she was ever grabbed by a man, it was better if she didn't resist, rather than be badly hurt or murdered.

Ernie grabbed Maggie's purse from the street and climbed into the back seat. He threw her purse on the floor of the car, then grabbed her hands and pulled them together behind her back. He took a length of hemp rope from his back pocket and tied her hands together.

"Let me go," Maggie pleaded.

Ernie grabbed her ankles and pulled them up to meet her hands. When she resisted Ernie put his weight on her legs. He tied her ankles to her hands and cinched the rope. He stood and slammed the car door. She sobbed uncontrollably and struggled.

Ernie got into the driver's seat and started the car. He turned on the headlights, slowly maneuvered the car away from the curb, and drove down the street.

Maggie tried to free herself by pulling with her hands and pushing with her feet. Her movements restricted her breathing. The smell of musty car seat and turpentine filled her nostrils. As the car left the darkened area, streetlamps illuminated the inside of the car. Maggie saw a vertical stripe design in the brown upholstered backseat. The back of the front seat was tan and had a thick rope that ran horizontally from one side of the seat-back to the other.

Then there were no more streetlights, only darkness. Maggie's mind raced. *Who is he? Why would he do this? Who would hear me if I screamed?* She sobbed, not knowing what to do. She pleaded with the man, "Let me go. Please, don't hurt me." The man didn't reply.

Elated with his catch, Ernie could hardly believe he was actually succeeding. He had failed too many times, trying to get into the women's cars. This time, in his car, it was working. Shaking with excitement and fear, Ernie looked in the rearview mirror, grinned, and said, "Just be quiet and I won't hurt you."

The worst scenarios ran through Maggie's mind. *What can I do if he wants to kill me? He has a knife. I don't want to be stabbed or cut. I'm trapped in this man's car and at his mercy.*

"Please let me go, don't hurt me," she begged the man again.

Ernie felt the thrill of the whole adventure and said again, "If you keep quiet, I won't hurt you." Still grinning, he drove on.

After what seemed like twenty minutes to Maggie, the car stopped. Ernie got out, took off his jacket, and threw it onto the driver's seat. He walked to the passenger side of the car and opened the back door. Maggie could smell the damp sand and creosote of the desert.

She screamed when Ernie touched the rope that bound her.

"I told you, if you keep quiet I won't hurt you."

Maggie grunted and stiffened. Ernie put his weight on her legs and untied her feet from her hands. "There's nowhere for you to run to, so you just do what I say."

Maggie feared they were far away from town and the man would kill her there in the desert.

She sat up, straightened her legs, and rubbed her wrists. Her limbs tingled, half asleep from the constriction of the rope and the prone position she'd been in. She looked around. The glow of the dome light made it difficult to see outside of the car. There was only darkness and some city lights in the distance.

Ernie sat in the back seat next to Maggie. He closed the car door and the dome light went out. She backed her body against the car door and cried.

"Take off your jacket."

"No, I won't do it. Please let me go."

Ernie grabbed her upper arms. Maggie screamed and trembled uncontrollably.

"The sooner we get this over with, the sooner you can go home."

Ernie pulled Maggie's jacket off. "If you fight me your clothes will get ripped off."

Maggie sniffed, wiped her face and did what Ernie wanted. He removed her vest, unbuttoned her blouse, and put them over the back of the front seat. He squatted on the passenger-side floor and told her, "Lay on your back." She reluctantly complied. He unbuttoned and unzipped her skirt, then pulled it off.

Ernie pawed aggressively and pulled at her slip, tearing the thin straps. When he tried to remove her underclothing, she clutched her bra with one hand and grabbed the top of her panties with the other. He pulled her panties off and removed her bra. Realizing he was still dressed, Ernie backed away onto the seat next to her. Maggie drew her legs to her chest. He frantically pulled off his Levi's and undershorts. She tried to look out the window for lights to a nearby house or a car. She saw only darkness and distant city lights.

Ernie wore only his sleeveless undershirt and glasses. He ordered her to lie on her back.

"No, don't do this," Maggie begged. "Please let me go." She sobbed as she pleaded.

Ernie pulled Maggie's legs down onto the seat, forced them apart and pushed her flat onto her back. He lay on top of her. Maggie felt his undershirt against her bare breasts. His breath smelled of cigarette smoke and stale beer. His glasses rubbed the left side of her head and his unshaven face pressed against her cheek.

He kissed her neck. She smelled like baby powder. He attempted to make penetration, but he could not perform. After several attempts he pushed away from her and sat up in the seat. Maggie tried to cover her herself with a hand between her legs and her arm across her breasts.

"You have probably done this before," Ernie said, staring down at her body, "so this won't hurt you."

"No, no, I've never been with a young man before. Don't do this to me."

The thought of having a virgin was the extra excitement Ernie needed. He pulled Maggie's arms away from her body. She yelped.

He pulled her hips toward him, pushed her on her back and climbed onto her. His breath stank. She struggled. "Don't fight me and I won't hurt you." Spittle struck Maggie's face when he spoke. She sobbed and looked away. Ernie made another attempt and this time he was successful.

Maggie lay there, bit her lip, and stared toward the ceiling in the backseat of the musty old car. She closed her eyes and wept while Ernie raped her.

When he released her, she pulled her knees to her chest, rolled onto her left side and sobbed. Ernie sat up in the seat next to her, breathing heavily. When he had caught his breath, he gave her a rag from the floor. A paintbrush fell out of it onto the floorboard. "Here, wipe yourself with this rag."

Ernie pulled on his undershorts and Levi's and got out of the car. He closed the back door, walked to the driver's side, and sat in the front seat. He lit a cigarette and looked at Maggie over the front seat. "Put your clothes on." As she dressed, Ernie asked her if she had any money.

"What?"

"Do you have any money?"

Maggie fumbled for her purse on the floorboard. She'd grabbed the paint brush, let go and found her purse. Maggie searched inside her purse and removed four ones. She handed the money forward toward the front seat and Ernie grabbed it.

"Now lie on your stomach, face down. I won't tie you up, because there's nowhere for you to run." Maggie lay on her stomach. Ernie got out of the car and opened the driver-side back door. He took Maggie's coat, covered her head, and closed the door. Ernie started the car, turned on the headlights and began to drive away.

When the car finally stopped again, Ernie looked over the backseat and said, "Whether you tell your mother what happened or not is none of my business, but pray for me."

Maggie was dumbfounded. When he let her out of the car she looked around. The nearby businesses were closed. She looked for someone, anyone, to yell to for help. She saw no one. The street signs read 12th Street and Bethany Home Road. Maggie knew where she was. The car drove south on 12th Street. She ran without looking back at the car. She thought for a moment to get a license plate number but couldn't make herself turn around. Maggie ran until she had to walk. She used her coat to wipe her face, and then she put the coat on, wrapped her arms around her body, and kept walking.

Maggie paused in front of 1014 East Citrus Way and gathered her courage. She patted her eyes with her hands, turned the front door knob, and walked into the house. Her eyes welled up all over again. She had thought she was cried out. She trembled and broke down as she told her sister, Sue Williamson, how a man in a light green car had abducted her, raped her, and taken her money.

TWO

THE MALE VOICE of the police radio dispatcher directed Patrol Officer John Page to 1014 East Citrus Way in reference to a possible rape and kidnapping. It was 2:08 a.m., Sunday morning March 3, 1963. Page listened, watched, and took notes while Maggie told him what had happened to her.

Maggie sat on the couch next to Sue Williamson, her older sister. Sue's husband, James Williamson, was sleeping in the master bedroom. Sue had chosen not to wake him. Maggie spoke to Officer Page in a shy, unassuming manner, recounting the entire ordeal from beginning to end. Page noted that Maggie didn't make much eye contact with him. She looked down at the floor as if she were ashamed. She didn't appear as hysterical or upset as other rape victims he had interviewed. She didn't cry, but did look as if she'd been crying. Page checked Maggie's hands and wrists for signs of rope burns and found none.

"When I called the police they said not to let Maggie bathe, use the restroom, change clothes, or even comb her hair," Sue said. "What can she do?"

"Rest assured that everything we ask of the two of you is meaningful and will eventually be explained." Page then turned to Maggie. "Thank you for being so patient. What we'll need to do next is to take your undergarments for evidence. If you ladies could go to

Maggie's bedroom, I'll need your slip, bra, and panties placed in a paper bag, like one from a grocery store.

"Yes, I'll get a bag from the kitchen."

"While you ladies do that I'll check in with my dispatcher." Page went outside to his patrol car to broadcast a partial description of the suspect and the suspect vehicle.

The police dispatcher repeated the description over the police radio to all units in the city. "Mexican male, six-foot, 175 pounds, white T-shirt, blue Levi's, black-rimmed glasses. Last seen driving an older model, very dirty, light green sedan with a brown interior."

Page found Sue waiting in the front room holding the grocery bag with Maggie's under garments when he returned. He paused a moment to organize his thoughts. "Could you answer a few questions for me, ma'am?"

Sue folded her hands in her lap. "Sure, if I can." She leaned forward and focused on the officer's words.

"How long has Maggie worked at the Paramount Theater?"

"Several months now."

Page wrote on his pad, then looked up. "During that time has she always ridden the bus?"

Sue thought for a moment. "She has on occasion ridden home with Reginald. He's another employee at the theater. They get off work at the same time and ride home on the bus. He has given Maggie a ride home in his car as much as two or three times a week."

"Does Maggie usually arrive home at the same time?"

"Well, sometimes she and Reginald stop and get something to eat first." Sue's body stiffened as she grasped the direction of the questioning. "Officer, Maggie has lived a somewhat sheltered life. She has not gone on very many dates."

Page made a note, took a breath, and let it out slowly. "Mrs. Williamson, I'm not intentionally trying to sound offensive. I have to ask some questions here and gather as much evidence as possible to show that Maggie is telling the truth."

"What are you saying? She wouldn't make something like this up—that's ridiculous."

"Well, all right. I'd like you to take her to the Good Samaritan

Hospital emergency room for an examination. Are you willing to do this?"

"Yes, of course, whatever we need to do."

"I'll meet you ladies at Good Sam then."

Sue handed the grocery bag with the clothing evidence to Page. "I'll have Maggie dress and we'll meet you there."

ON THE WAY to hospital, Page notified his sergeant of the situation, who in turn arranged for night detectives Kyle Gourdoux and Don Davis to go to Good Sam and take over the investigation.

Page briefed the detectives in the emergency room and gave them the paper bag with Maggie's undergarments. He introduced the detectives to Maggie and Sue, then wrote a supplemental report and went back on patrol.

Maggie sat on a chilly Naugahyde examination table, in a gown that didn't fit right, while an RN prepared her for a complete examination that would include a Pap smear test. Doctors Lekos and Clemenger, working together and whom would later serve as witnesses for each other, collected blood, urine, hair, and other samples.

Doctor Lekos wrote in Maggie's hospital chart:

NO VISIBLE MARKS, BRUISES, OR ABRAISIONS COULD BE FOUND.

He further documented taking a large amount of sperm from the vagina of the victim. Both doctors reported they didn't believe the victim to have been a virgin prior to the alleged rape.

After the examination Detectives Gourdoux and Davis met with Maggie in a private lounge and asked her to tell them, again, what happened? She began from when she left the Paramount Theater. They found the details to be consistent with the first two times she had told her story, once to her sister and the second time to Officer Page. Maggie remembered a few more elements that she had forgotten. Then she quoted the suspect's departing comment again: *"Whether you tell your mother what has happened or not is none of my business, but pray for me."* Maggie ended her story with how she had run home.

Gourdoux leaned forward in his chair. "When he tied your hands and feet, did he use one piece of rope or two?"

Maggie thought for a moment. "I'm not sure."

"Okay. Can you tell me the order in which he removed your clothing?"

Maggie shook her head. "I'm sorry, I don't remember."

Gourdoux shifted in his chair. "Maggie, are you certain of the man's race?"

She stared at her hands clasped together in her lap. "I think he was Mexican, but he didn't have an accent...I suppose he could be Italian."

"Well, did he touch you in any particular manner or fondle any parts of your body?"

"Not really. He did kiss my neck once."

Gourdoux looked at Davis and shrugged his shoulders. Both were thinking that Maggie couldn't remember details that she should have.

Gourdoux sat back in his chair. "Do you think you could recognize this guy if you saw him again?"

Maggie nodded. "Yes, I'm certain. I'll recognize him."

GOURDOUX AND DAVIS drove to Phoenix Police headquarters at 17 South 2nd Avenue, where they wrote the original kidnapping, rape, and robbery report on the Margaret Fair case—DR #63-08380, dated March 3, 1963. Although three crimes had been committed against the victim—kidnapping, rape, and robbery—the police report was titled with the most serious crime: rape.

The six-story stone building then used by the police department dated from 1929. It housed the Maricopa County Courtrooms and the offices of the City of Phoenix officials. Jail facilities were on the fifth and sixth floors. Police headquarters had space on both the first floor and in the basement at the southwest side of the building. Along with detectives and supervisors, there were dispatchers, the Records and Information Bureau (R & I Bureau), and the detective bureaus.

Gourdoux and Davis attached the supplemental report authored by Officer Page and placed their completed report in the day-shift sergeant's in-box.

The detectives were leaving for home when two patrol officers brought in a man for drunk and disorderly. The handcuffed suspect bumped unsteadily from side to side between the two officers, as they stood in front of the booking desk. The detectives stopped and listened as the arresting officers explained the circumstances of the arrest to the booking sergeant.

"This older-model Buick was driving erratically, going eastbound on McDowell, Sarge," said one officer. "I switched on the red light and siren and he takes off. We chase him into Scottsdale, just past the Cross Cut Canal…"

The second officer stepped toward the desk, nudging the suspect forward, and continued the conversation. "Yeah, then he runs off the road and crashes. We run up to see if he's all right and the driver's door comes flying open and he tries to run."

"Yeah, but he's too drunk," the first officer chimed in, "he only gets about ten feet and falls down. Then we take him into custody without a fight."

The sergeant looked up from the blotter. "Yeah, so who is he?"

"Here's his license, Sarge. Says he's Billy Gene Morrison."

Gourdoux looked the suspect over and tapped Davis on the arm with the back of his hand. "Five-foot-eleven inches, 175, black hair, white T-shirt and Levi's."

Davis turned to Gourdoux. "You don't think…"

"It could be. Stranger things have happened."

The detectives retrieved their report, added Billy Gene Morrison as a possible suspect, and notified their sergeant before heading home. The detectives' sergeant telephoned the day shift assaults detective, Sergeant Nealis, at home at 4:00 a.m. and gave him the basics of the Margaret Fair rape case. Because there was a possible suspect in custody on an unrelated D & D charge, Nealis called two day-shift detectives at their homes, despite the early hour. Detectives Wilfred "Bill" Young and Edwin Smith reported to the station and took charge of the investigation.

After reviewing the report and all the supplements, Young and Smith decided to conduct a live lineup with suspect Billy Gene Morrison. Detective Bobby Manning drove to the victim's house on

East Citrus Way. Sue Williamson answered the door and then awakened a sleepy Maggie Fair.

"Here, Maggie." Sue removed a light blue button-down blouse and a gray pleated skirt from the closet. "Get dressed. There's a detective waiting for you."

Maggie yawned and rubbed an eye with the heel of her hand. She stared at nothing for a moment. Then the tears came. "I don't believe this. I've been through enough already and I need some rest."

Sue dropped down on the bed and put an arm around her sister. "I don't like it either, but the police arrested a man, and they want you to look at him."

"What if it's him? What do I do?" Maggie' eyes were wide open. "What would you do?"

"Well if it's him, I'd have to say it's him."

"But I'm afraid." Maggie clung to Sue.

Sue took hold of Maggie's shoulders. "You'll be fine."

"Are going with me?"

"No dear, I have to take care of things here and Jim expects me to be here."

Maggie sobbed.

"You're strong, you'll be fine Maggie."

MAGGIE ARRIVED AT police headquarters with Detective Manning at 9:00 a.m. Detectives Young and Smith took the jail elevator to the men's jail on the fifth floor. They requested that the jail officer pull Billy Gene Morrison's cell door card. The card displayed the inmate's booking information and had a 1x1-inch black and white photo of him attached. Young then asked the jail officer to pull out four inmates whose door card photos looked similar to Morrison's. The men were handcuffed separately and then shackled together with a chain that snaked through their ankle cuffs. The jailer pulled Morrison from his cell and logged the inmates out in the logbook. Detective Young signed for custody of the inmates.

When the elevator stopped on the first floor the shackled inmates were marched over to Interview Room One. Jail officers placed the five men in a line, shoulder to shoulder, against the back wall. A white 8½x11-inch card with a large black number on it hung around each inmate's neck. They numbered in sequence one through five. With the light on inside the room, the inmates could not see out through the mirrored door.

Detective Young brought Maggie over to Interview Room One. They stood there, looking into the room through the mirrored door.

"There are five men inside this room here," Young said. "They can't see us while the light is on inside the room. All they see is a mirrored glass door on their side. Do you understand that you're safe here?"

"Yes, I think so."

"Okay." Young steadied Maggie's shoulders and faced her toward the mirrored door.

Maggie looked through the glass, and said softly, "You said they can't see me, right?"

"Don't be afraid, they can't see you."

"Uh-huh, okay."

"Maggie, I want you to look at each one of these men—start with the one on the left. Tell me if you recognize any of 'em." The detective's voice was slow but steady. "Now, if you do recognize one of these men, tell me where you recognize him from."

Maggie looked at each man for a long time. "He's not here. None of them are him." Maggie sighed and lowered her head. She took a few deep breaths.

Detective Young walked Maggie over to Interview Room Two and asked her to wait there.

Detective Smith then had Officer Monroe photograph the men in the lineup. An officer escorted the inmates back to their cells.

The detectives walked into Interview Room Two, where Maggie sat at a table.

Young asked questions and Smith made notes. "Can you tell us what happened to you again, Maggie? I'd like you to start at the beginning."

Maggie took a deep breath and blew it out slowly. "I got off work at the Paramount Theater at 11:20 p.m." Her head bobbed slightly in a rhythm with her words. "I walked to First Street and Monroe with Reginald Fertig. We waited by the bus bench until about 11:45 p.m."

Maggie told the entire story for the fourth time without varying from the three previous versions. She was able to add a few more details but she recounted the same sequence of events with the same haunting ending—the man telling her, *Whether you tell your mother what has happened or not is none of my business, but pray for me.*

Detective Young leaned in, propping his elbows on the table. The backs of his fingers rested on his cheeks. "Maggie, can you tell us more about where the man took you in his car?"

Maggie exhaled and looked down at her hands. She wrung her hands, took a deep breath, and hoped that the detective would believe her this time. "The man drove for about twenty minutes and made several turns. I don't know where we ended up...I'm sorry."

"The suspect—did he have any scars, marks, or tattoos?"

Maggie swallowed, thought for moment, and took a breath. "It was too dark. If he did, I didn't see any."

Young noticed that Maggie had pulled her hands to her lap. Her shoulders were slumped and she stared down at the floor. "You're doing just fine, Maggie. I know you haven't had much sleep, and this won't take much longer. Now, can you tell us anything more about the car?"

Maggie closed her eyes, lifted her chin, and inhaled. "Well, it was an older model, maybe a 1955. It might've been a Chevrolet or a Ford. It was light green...and it was cleaner on the outside than on the inside."

"Tell me about the inside of the car."

Maggie put her hands together between her knees. "The inside had brown upholstery. It was very um...shabby. It smelled funny. It smelled like paint...or um, turpentine. And there was a paintbrush on the floor."

"How big was the paintbrush? You know, how long was it and how wide? Was it new or used?"

"Um, I would say it was about three inches wide at the brush part, but I don't know if it was new or used, it was dark."

"Can you tell us more about the backseat...anything unusual?"

"Um, on the back of the front seat, there was a rope that went across the back of the seat. I think maybe for someone to grab hold of to pull themselves out off of the seat to get out of the car."

"What can you tell us about this rope, Margaret? What did it look like? How big around was it, and was there anything special about the rope?"

"The rope was about a half-inch around and had these small hairs coming from it."

"That might be a Manila rope." Young paused, thinking about it. "Maggie, could you excuse us for a moment?"

YOUNG AND SMITH conferred in the hallway.

"What's the evidence telling us," Young asked, "and is it the same as what Maggie's saying?"

"She can't give any details of the location of the assault," Smith said.

Young offered a pack of smokes to Smith, then drew a metal lighter from his pants pocket. The cigarette bobbed in his mouth as he spoke. "Her story is consistent but there's too many holes in it." He flipped the hinged top of the lighter open, his thumb rotating the flint wheel in one quick motion, then flipped the lighter's lid closed.

Smith lit his cigarette with a butane lighter and took a drag. Smoke came from his mouth along with his words. "The doctors said she didn't have any bruises or abrasions anywhere on her body and that she wasn't a virgin, although she said she was."

"So we've got to get her to tell us the truth?" Young said.

WHEN YOUNG AND Smith reentered the interview room Maggie stopped twirling her hair, put her hands in her lap, and looked down. The detectives remained standing.

"Rape is a serious accusation, Maggie," Young said firmly. "You know you could be charged with filing a false police report."

Maggie looked up at Young and froze. Her eyes widened, she blinked quickly several times, and her mouth fell open. "What? I wouldn't lie!"

"We want to be sure you're being truthful." Young put his palms on the table, paused, and looked down at Maggie. "One tool that we use to help us find out the truth is a lie detector. Technically, it's called a polygraph machine." Young let the words hang.

Maggie swallowed, closed her eyes, and shook her head. *They don't believe me.* She willed herself not to cry.

"Maggie, would you be willing to submit to a polygraph examination?"

"Right now?"

Young stood straight and waved his hands, palms out. "No, no, you've been through enough. This would be in a few days."

Maggie looked up at Young. "If that's what's required, I guess so."

IT WAS AFTER 11a.m. when the detectives drove Maggie back to her home. Traffic was moderate with a couple of church services letting out onto 7th Street. They asked her if she could pick out a car resembling the suspect's vehicle. A few minutes later, Maggie pointed out a 1955 Chevy and said, "It was like that one—it looks similar, but I can't be sure."

Young drove east on Marlette from 7th Street. "Is this about where you were abducted?"

Maggie looked out of the car window, then looked down. "Yes, across from the building with three sevens on it."

Young stopped the car in front of 777 East Marlette. The detectives got out and searched the area for evidence that could lead to the suspect. They found none.

At twelve noon Maggie finally laid her head on her pillow. She desired sleep and easy dreams. She had already lived a nightmare.

THREE

IN 1962, AFTER four years with the Phoenix Police Department as a patrol officer, Carroll Cooley completed the rigorous process of becoming a detective. He was first assigned to the Property Crimes Bureau. He began working cases involving burglaries, thefts, criminal damage, and criminal trespassing.

1963, Cooley drew a reassignment to Sergeant Nealis's squad. These detectives solved cases involving assaults, kidnappings, and rapes. Cooley's new squad was known as the Crimes Against Persons Detail. Nealis had a reputation for solving crimes. As a detective sergeant, he expected no less from the detectives assigned to him. These detectives were not known as the most physically fit squad on the department. They lost sleep because they were called out at night. They had bad eating habits. Nevertheless, they solved crimes assigned and cleared cases. Cooley, now their newest member, was only twenty-seven years old. He maintained a fitness program and stayed in shape. He would work as hard, if not harder, on this squad because he knew the sergeant and his senior peers expected results in solving the cases assigned to him.

Cooley digested and retained the information gleaned from reading the police reports assigned to him. He learned to identify patterns of behavior and link cases together by the suspect's method of operation, or MO. He also learned how to conduct effective interviews and interrogations.

MONDAY MORNING, MARCH 4, 1963, Detective Sergeant Seymour Nealis sat down behind his World War II vintage desk, sipped his coffee, and started going over police reports from the weekend. His chair, like his vintage desk, was made of metal covered with gray paint. Sergeant Nealis, a stocky man in his mid-thirties, read each report, assigned each one to a detective, and logged all the reports into the Departmental Report book, known as the DR log. He reassigned the Margaret Fair rape case to Detective Cooley.

Carroll Cooley's Monday morning was filled with reviewing reports, telephoning victims, and obtaining their medical records from local hospitals. After reading the newly assigned rape case, Cooley conferred with two of the detectives who had been called out on the weekend, Young and Smith.

That afternoon, Cooley drove to 1014 East Citrus Way in his assigned detective's car—a 1960 Plymouth Fury, basic black, with four doors. The fins on the rear quarter panels rose sharply in a curve with a circular medallion in the center. The headlight eyebrow trim curved around the side of the fender to a spot above the wheel arch. Under the hood was a SonoRamic Commando V-8 with an automatic transmission. The car was fast, but the brakes didn't work very well.

Cooley turned east from 10th Street into the cul-de-sac of East Citrus Way. He drove to the end, turned the car around, and parked in front of 1014—a white, single-story wood-framed house with three bedrooms and a carport.

Cooley straightened his tie as he walked toward Margaret Fair's front door. He fished out a roll of Certs breath mints from his suit coat pocket, slid down the wrapper, and unraveled the gold foil to reveal a circular, white breath mint. He pulled the top mint off with his teeth and put the roll back in his jacket pocket. After completing this ritual, Detective Cooley rang the doorbell.

Susanne Williamson answered the door, and Cooley found himself looking at an attractive woman who wore a flowered print apron over a tan chiffon blouse and tan slacks. Cooley surmised that Susanne stood about five-foot-six. She was thirty-six years old.

"I'm Detective Cooley with the Phoenix Police Department," Cooley said, displaying his badge and credentials.

"Please come in."

Cooley thanked her, stepped inside, and stated his business. "I would like to interview Margaret Fair. I'm hoping she can give me a little more detail about her attacker, the location of the attack, and the car he drove."

"Well, have a seat, Inspector."

"Mrs. Williamson, please refer to me as Detective or Officer—inspectors, I think, work at the post office."

"I meant no offense," Williamson said. "Please have a seat." She gestured toward a chair.

Cooley sat on the edge of a chair near a coffee table. Suzanne sat on a matching couch on the other side of the coffee table.

"Maggie's at work at the Paramount right now," Sue said. "She won't be home until later tonight."

Cooley nodded. "Could you tell me a little bit about Margaret?"

"Well, she's a very shy and naive girl. I talked to her about the incident at length so that she would stop thinking it was her fault. We now have my brother-in-law walk her home from the bus stop. You know, so nothing else happens."

"That's good." Cooley took a notepad from his inside jacket pocket. "Who is your brother-in-law?"

"His name is Paul Henkle. He just got out of the Marines. He can take care of himself, and we trust that he'll be able to walk Maggie home safely, if that's what you're asking."

Cooley wrote a note and then looked up. "How can I get in touch with Mr. Henkle?"

"He's not here right now, but he'll be staying with us for a while."

Checking his notes, Cooley flipped a page back in his notepad. "The responding officer's report stated that Maggie had no marks, bruises, scars, or rope burns on her arms. Do you know if she resisted her attacker?"

"That may be my fault, Detective," Sue said, looking down. "I told Maggie if she were ever caught in such a position she should not resist. I told her she might be beaten or harmed worse...maybe even killed if she tried to fight."

"I see." Cooley turned another page in his notepad.

"Detective, Maggie has been through a lot, and it's been insinuated that she made this whole story up. She was a virgin, even though the doctors who examined her say she wasn't."

"Why do you suppose the doctors thought she wasn't a virgin?"

"Well, I don't know. Maggie's a grown woman. I think maybe the doctors were probably mistaken, that's all."

"I'd like to talk to Margaret at police headquarters as soon as possible. I'll need to gather more information in order to find the suspect." Cooley stood up, took out his badge wallet, and singled out a business card. "Here's my business card." He leaned forward over the coffee table, handing Williamson the card. "Would you ask Mr. Henkle if he should see anyone suspicious or a suspicious vehicle while he's walking Margaret home to please call me?"

"I will, Detective. Thank you."

COOLEY DROVE TO the Paramount Theatre at 2nd Avenue and Monroe Street. A film was already playing in the theater so no one stood in line at the box office windows. He presented his credentials to Margaret Fair, the young woman seated in the box office. She wore her theater uniform—a black vest, a white blouse, and a black skirt.

"Listen, Margaret, I know you've been through a lot, and I really need to clarify some of the information in the police report." Maggie replied, but Cooley couldn't make out what she said. "Could you speak up a little? I can hardly hear you through the glass." Cooley put his ear to the 4-inch hole in the teller window and listened.

"I can't talk right now, Detective," Maggie said softly, but loud enough for him to hear her. "I'm the only one in the box office, so I can't leave."

"Do you get a break?"

"I really don't want to talk about it at work, Detective." She didn't look up from sorting tickets for the evening show.

"Would sometime tomorrow be better for you?"

"Well, I don't have to work tomorrow," Maggie said.

"Could I come by your house and talk to you? Your sister Susanne is welcome to be there—would that be all right?"

"I suppose so."

"Okay, I'll see you tomorrow morning around nine o'clock then."

THE FOLLOWING MORNING, Carroll Cooley and Detective Dick Golden returned to East Citrus Way.

"I'd like to interview Margaret at police headquarters," Cooley told Sue Williamson. "It's very important that we go over everything together and determine what exactly happened. This could lead us to the suspect and his vehicle."

Maggie gave Sue a woeful look.

"I'll bring Margaret back home myself, as soon as we've finished the interview," Cooley said.

Maggie went to her bedroom and emerged a few minutes later wearing an olive green dress. She said nothing during the ride to police headquarters.

COOLEY PARKED ON 2nd Avenue at the front of the steps of City Hall's west entrance. The entrance lay under the watchful eyes of two eagles carved into the sandstone a full story above the ornate brass doors at the top of the stairway. The police public entrance was located under the staircase.

The detectives led Maggie through the doors underneath the staircase. Walnut framed doors enclosing clear glass panes lined the marble floor of the airless hallway, the color of the wood had gone dark in the dim light. A door on the right side of the hallway opened into the police department. There were a few offices against the walls, and detectives' desks filled the center of the large room. The room hummed with the sounds of typewriters, paper being shuffled, and indistinct one-sided phone conversations.

Maggie smelled a whiff of cigarette smoke blended with the smell of fresh perked coffee. A phone stopped ringing when a detective picked up the receiver.

Cooley and Maggie continued to Interview Room Two. Cooley pulled out one of the two chairs and Maggie slid into the seat and scooted close to the table.

"I've got to get some paperwork. I'll be right back," Cooley said. He looked back and asked Maggie, "Would you like some coffee or a cold beverage?"

"No thank you," Maggie muttered, without making eye contact.

The door closed behind Cooley. Maggie sat alone, her hands clasped together in her lap. She looked around. The walls were covered with white acoustic tiles drilled with random holes. The tiles enveloped the walls and ceiling. Their pattern was interrupted only by the bright fluorescent lights suspended high above her head. The room stank of stale cigarette smoke.

The heavy armless chair was uncomfortable, even with the gray Naugahyde padding. Maggie shifted in her seat. She remembered her interview in this very room with detectives Young and Smith. She hoped the feeling of being trapped, isolated, and being thought of as a liar would be dispelled. She reminded herself. *I'm the victim, not the suspect.*

Cooley reappeared, closed the door behind him, and put a manila folder on the table. He pulled out a chair and settled into it, then opened the folder and silently read the first page. Then he placed his forearms on the table, laced his fingers together, and looked at Maggie. "Is it possible that you could be mistaken about this event?"

Maggie's lips quivered and she looked down at the table.

"Margaret, is it possible that you've become involved with someone, a man, and on Saturday night, you came home late after being with that man, and made a police report?"

Maggie wrung her hands in her lap. Her mouth went dry, and she swallowed. *What are you saying? The man raped me.* Maggie nodded her head and heard her own soft voice say, "Yes."

Cooley didn't understand what Maggie was saying "yes" to. He put a legal-size notepad on the table and turned to a clean sheet. "Margaret, tell me the complete story of what happened to you…and don't leave anything out."

Maggie blinked a few times, swallowed, took a breath, and looked down at her hands.

Cooley leaned in closer to her. "Could you do that for me?"

Maggie told Detective Cooley what had happened to her that Saturday night after she'd left work at the Paramount Theater. She added as much detail as she could remember. Her story remained consistent with the original report. Cooley wrote in silence.

"When I told what happened to me to the first officer, I said I struggled to untie the rope. But I didn't try very hard…that's why I probably didn't have any bruises or rope burns."

After going over Maggie's statement twice, Cooley left the interview room to have a cigarette. He didn't know if Margaret was telling the whole truth at this point, and he knew he wasn't asking the right questions to solicit the correct answers from her. He had to ask questions that would allow her to tell the whole truth. He thought he was a good interrogator, and he wanted to find a way to allow Margaret to be comfortable and feel safe enough to tell her story truthfully.

He thought Margaret might implicate a boyfriend, maybe Reginald Fertig. Maybe she had made the police report to cover for a date with Reginald after he had brought her home late. If not, Cooley knew he would have to gather more information and locate the suspect and his vehicle.

Cooley went over to the police records and information section, the R & I Bureau. There he requested two books with photographs of known sex offenders, both white and Mexican. Returning to the interview room, he laid the books on the table in front of Margaret. He remained standing and spoke in an even tone. "Margaret, these books contain photographs of known sex offenders in Phoenix. I would like you to take your time, look at each picture, and tell me if you recognize any of these men."

Maggie opened the first book and looked at all of the 2x3-inch photographs, held on heavy pages by black, triangular-shaped mounts. She wanted so badly to see a photograph of her rapist in the book. She looked hard and long at each picture. Then she looked a second time and then a third time. She looked through the second book with the same tenaciousness. Maggie paused looked at Detective Cooley and said, "None of these men are the man who raped me."

Cooley drove Maggie home after two hours of attempting to

find out the whole truth.

After pleasantries, Cooley said, "Mrs. Williamson, Margaret and I had a long talk and I showed her the police department's books of photographs of known rapist we have on file and we have not been able to identify a suspect. Although I feel we are closer to the getting to the bottom of this we have not found any evidence or witnesses that would lead us to a suspect."

"Is there anything else that Maggie or I can do at this point?" Sue asked.

"If you can think of anyone who might commit these types of crimes that you or Margaret may have had contact with in the past, I would like their name and information."

"I assure you detective there hasn't been anyone of this character that we would have had contact with."

"Well, I'll keep you both updated as the case develops."

FOUR

THE KIDNAP, RAPE, and robbery of Margaret Fair was Ernie Miranda's most successful venture, if you could call it that. To prepare himself he had walked the alleys and parking lots of downtown Phoenix, his chosen hunting ground. Moving in daylight, he would follow women from their workplaces to their nearby houses or apartments. He would then return under the cover of darkness, peep through bedroom windows, and watch women undress as they got ready for bed.

If a woman leaves a curtain open, it's an invitation. It means she wants me.

His first attempt at trapping and raping a woman occurred in November 1962. It was late afternoon in Phoenix, a cool 58 degrees. Ernie knew it would only get cooler when night fell. On this particular Tuesday afternoon, November 27th, he had driven from his home in Mesa and pulled his Packard into a space west of Central Avenue on Monroe Street, one block away from the Paramount Theatre. The car would not look out of place. People would assume someone had parked there to attend a movie.

Ernie roamed the blocks north of Monroe from 5th Avenue to 3rd Street, passing by businesses that reminded him of women he had previously followed home. He knew five women who worked late at the Phoenix Credit Bureau on 1st Street—well, he didn't know them personally, but he had watched each of them and he knew their names. He once followed a woman from the credit bureau to her apartment at 404 East McKinley. He hadn't returned later because the woman's husband came home.

Ernie lit a cigarette, took a drag, held it in his lungs, and then blew the smoke out through his nose. He thought he blended in pretty well in downtown Phoenix. He bathed every Saturday, and he wore a clean tan jacket with a dress shirt and tan pants. His four-day growth of beard made him look older than his twenty-one years.

Ernie thought he was smarter and smoother than the other men who followed women around on the street. He'd seen a guy the previous evening, circling the block in a blue 1958 Oldsmobile, watching the same beautiful woman Ernie had followed to McKinley Street. She had passed by him on the sidewalk where he had been loitering, smoking a cigarette. He'd read her name tag: SANDY COE.

The man in the Oldsmobile had driven up next to the woman and whistled at her through the open passenger window. She ignored him until the guy called to her. She looked back, not recognizing the man, and kept walking. He pulled his car in close to the curb and asked if she wanted a ride. She continued to ignore him and walked east on McKinley Street.

Ernie followed them both at a distance, watching and listening. The man drove closer still, stopped his car, and asked if he could take her out to dinner. "I'd like to get better acquainted with you," the man said. *Maybe that's what older white guys say,* Ernie thought. After all, the man had to be thirty. Ernie heard Mrs. Coe tell the man that she was married and her husband was waiting for her. The man circled the block several more times before he finally drove away.

Now after 8:30 p.m. Ernie could see his breath in the night air. The streetlights had come on and the banks and other businesses had closed. Ernie went unnoticed as he watched people leave work for their homes. He had a new plan. This one was different and it excited him. He needed only one woman—a dedicated woman, one who worked late and walked to her car alone.

BARBARA SUE McDANIEL left her workplace and began her evening trek to the Western Parking Lot on the southwest corner of 2nd Street and Fillmore. She knew her long shifts at the First

National Bank at Central Avenue and Van Buren Street would eventually pay off. Hard work always did. Barbara was twenty-two years old and streetwise enough to walk with her head up and her eyes open. Her father had always told her that if you're walking alone you have to be aware of your surroundings.

Barbara noticed a man illuminated by the street lamp ahead. He wore a tan jacket and pants. He was walking about a half-block south of her, across the street, at 2nd and Taylor. She didn't pay much attention to him, because there was some distance between them. It didn't occur to her that the man had been walking parallel with her since 1st and Van Buren streets.

When Barbara reached the driveway of the Western Parking Lot the automatic gate arm was down and there was no attendant on duty. Other second-shift workers' cars lined the lot. Barbara recognized many of them. She walked to the last row near the alley and continued down eight spaces before she reached her 1960 Ford Galaxie.

Barbara looked around and saw no one in the parking lot. She took off her coat and purse, swung her car door open, and eased into the front seat. She piled her coat and purse on the passenger side and shut the door. She pumped the gas pedal several times and then turned the ignition key. The starter motor cranked but the engine wouldn't start. She pumped the gas pedal and tried the ignition again. No go. Another try…the engine nearly kicked over but it still wouldn't start.

Barbara smelled gasoline and realized she had flooded the carburetor. She could hear her father's voice in her head: *Don't panic, Barbara, all you have to do is wait a few minutes for the gas to dissipate. Then you'll be on your way.*

A knock on her car window nearly sent her through the roof. Her hands flew to her chest and she gasped when she saw it was the man in the tan jacket.

Ernie spoke loud enough to be heard through the car window. "Excuse me, ma'am , could you tell me the time?"

Barbara thought for a second, looked into the man's face, and spoke back to him in a voice just as loud as his own. "I'm not sure. I think it's about 8:45."

Timothy W. Moore - Clark Lohr

The man sniffed the air. "Seems like your car is flooded."

Ernie jerked Barbara's door open and pushed his way in. Barbara screamed. Ernie shoved her with his hips until he had jolted her into the middle of the front seat and he was behind the steering wheel. Barbara screamed louder. Ernie clamped his hand over her mouth.

"Don't scream if you don't want to get hurt," Ernie said.

Barbara's eyes widened. She nodded her head and Ernie took his hand away.

"What do you want?" Barbara asked.

Ernie didn't reply. He started the car and drove it to the exit. The gate arm was down. When the car stopped, Barbara jumped at the passenger door, trying to snatch her coat and purse on the way. Ernie grabbed Barbara's shoulder as the gate arm rose and jerked her back. He sped through the exit, the Ford fishtailing as it turned north onto 2nd Street.

Ernie made a quick left and the centrifugal force pulled Barbara toward the passenger door. Ernie yanked her back and kept driving, speeding through the night toward McKinley Street. He made another left, then another, and the car lurched recklessly into the dark alley between 1st and 2nd streets. When they were halfway down the alley Ernie slammed his foot on the brake pedal and the car slid to a stop, dust and gravel flying everywhere. Barbara put her hands up to keep from being thrown into the dashboard.

Ernie shut off the headlights and killed the engine, then reached back over his shoulder and locked the driver-side door. Barbara glimpsed at a sign on the back side of a building and realized they were now parked behind the Phoenix Credit Bureau.

Ernie spun around in the seat and lunged at her, grabbing her shoulders. He put his face inches from hers. "I'm not going to rape you." His eyes darted back and forth, looking first into one of Barbara's eyes, then into the other. "If I was, I would have done it in the parking lot."

Barbara tried to scream, but no sound came out. Ernie straddled her lap, putting his full weight on her. His breath stank of cigarette smoke. He put his hands on her blouse and squeezed her breasts.

32

"What are you doing?" she screamed, trying to push him off.

Ernie clambered over her and pushed the passenger door lock down. "Move over," he said, and pushed Barbara's hips toward the driver's seat. She scooted over and tried to push him away, batting at his hand with hers.

"Move some more," Ernie said.

Barbara grabbed the steering wheel and pulled herself toward the door, reaching for the lock. Ernie clutched her shoulders and spun her toward him. She tensed, facing her attacker, put her hands up, and took a breath. *I'm not going to cry, I'm going to talk.*

"I'll give you the car if you want," Barbara said. "Is that what you want—my car?"

"I don't want your car."

Barbara tried to distract Ernie with more questions. "Are you religious? Are you a Catholic?"

"I don't believe in God. I'm an atheist."

"So are you from Phoenix?"

"No."

"Oh, where're you from?"

"I—I'm from Texas."

"You don't have a Texas accent."

"That's enough talking," Ernie shouted.

He ran his hands over her breasts and down to her hips. She flailed at him. He tried to force her down on the seat. She pushed hard on his chest with both hands and tried to sit up straight. Ernie squeezed her breasts again and clutched at her hips. "Do you want your clothes ripped off?"

"Of course not, stop touching me." She slapped at his hands, breathing harder now as she tried to push him away. She glanced around for help but the car windows were fogging up on the inside. Outside, there was only darkness.

"Then why fight me if you don't want your clothes ripped off?" Ernie pulled out his knife and opened it with one hand.

Barbara heard the blade lock in place and watched Ernie move the knife toward her stomach. "Look," Barbara said, staring directly into his face, "there are cops all over this area." She was breathing hard, her mind racing. Tears came.

Ernie lightly ran the blade across her stomach and pulled her to him. "If I have to, I'll use force."

"Wait, just wait," Barbara said. "If you're going to do this, I can drive to my apartment. At least it'll be more comfortable."

Just like Mrs. Coe said to the white guy, Ernie thought. *"My husband's waiting for me."*

"No, no," he said. "You might have some friends there waiting for you.

"I don't know what you're talking about," she said.

"Just lay down on the seat."

"I prefer to drive to my apartment."

Ernie kept the knife at Barbara's stomach. "Okay," he said, "then give me your money." He shifted back, lifted Barbara's brown purse from the floorboard, and handed it to her.

Barbara reached into the purse, pulled out her matching billfold, and unsnapped the change purse. Her hands shook as she poured a dollar's worth of change into Ernie's open hand. He shoved the money into his front pants pocket. Barbara closed the billfold.

Ernie raised the knife and jabbed the air, inches from her chest. "No. Give me the bills, too". He took the bills when Barbara opened the wallet, stuffing them into his pants pocket. He picked up Barbara's coat from the floorboard, and got out on the passenger side. He yelled back in to the car, "Now don't go away!"

Barbara hesitated, clutched her purse, and opened the door. Ernie circled the car and blocked her way. He still held her coat. Barbara drew back and watched as Ernie used her coat in an attempt to wipe away his fingerprints. He began with the window on the driver's side. He wiped off the armrest and the steering wheel, then pressed the coat into Barbara's chest, pinning her against the car seat. He leaned down, once again putting his face inches from hers.

"I'm sorry this had to happen to you, and I hope it doesn't happen again—but if it does, I hope you can talk them out of it, like you did me. This time I'll just take your money." Ernie pushed himself off of Barbara's chest, slammed the car door closed, and walked briskly up the alley toward McKinley Street.

Barbara's hands shook as she locked the driver-side door. She began crying as she fumbled with the ignition key. The engine caught and she roared out of the alley, heading southbound. The car slid sideways and bounced onto Pierce Street, tires squealing until they gripped the concrete. The car fishtailed, but Barbara regained control and turned east onto 2nd Street. She drove south on 2nd Street, blowing through traffic signals and stop signs, then she came to her senses and stopped at a red light at Washington Street. She began taking slow, deep breaths, forcing herself to calm down.

When the light turned green, Barbara pulled through the intersection. She wiped the tears from her cheeks and straightened her clothes. Her arms felt heavy, draped over the steering wheel. She forced her hands up the wheel to the ten–two position.

I can't talk to my dad about this right now...

Barbara continued down Washington Street. Her Ford Galaxie seemed to drive itself across the Mill Avenue Bridge into Tempe. Still dazed, Barbara drove east on Broadway to Rural Road. She tried to snap out of it, but kept replaying the incident. She began to realize the man had assaulted her, taken her money, and tried to rape her.

I got away, I wasn't stabbed or raped, and the man didn't get my car... The SOB took my last eight bucks, and I don't get paid until Friday. She tried to laugh but only started crying again. The Galaxie turned itself into a narrow driveway at 702 Broadmoor Drive and came to a stop. Barbara put her head on the steering wheel and sobbed.

Mary Ann Dingman looked out her front window and noticed her best friend's green Ford Galaxie had just pulled into her driveway. Mary pushed through her front door and ran down the walkway, hugging herself and rubbing her shoulders to shake off the night chill.

"Barbie, are you okay?" Mary Ann reached down and tried to open Barbara's car door. Barbara lifted her head and looked into her friend's eyes. She unlocked the car door and Mary Ann opened it and asked, "Oh my gosh, are you all right?"

"I've had a tough day," Barbara said.

"Let's get you inside." Mary Ann walked Barbara into the house.

"There was this man. He got in the car with me. He was touching me." Barbara's eyes welled up and she shuddered.

"Barbie, sit down over here on the couch," Mary Ann said. "Oh honey, that's it—sit there and let me get you a tissue."

Mary Ann went to the kitchen and returned with a glass of water and a box of tissues. Barbara took a sip of water, took a breath, and then took a gulp of water. She put the glass on the coffee table, sniffed, and wiped her face with a tissue. Mary Ann held Barbara until she was able to tell the whole story. She hung on every word, blinking in disbelief.

"Oh Barbie, you did great. You really did. You're safe now."

"I never saw him before," Barbara said, "but I'll never forget what he looked like. I was scared to death."

"You did well, honey, and you got away. You'll have to call the police right now and tell them."

Barbara lifted Mary Ann's black rotary telephone from the table beside the couch and dialed the operator who then connected her to the Tempe Police Department. Barbara briefly described the incident and where it took place.

The police operator's voice was nasal, almost robotic. "The crime occurred in Phoenix, not in Tempe. The Tempe Police Department does not have jurisdiction there. You have to call the Phoenix Police to report this crime. Do you understand?"

"But *you're* the police," Barbara said. "I have to make a report so you can find the guy. I thought he was going to kill me."

"You still have to go to your home in Phoenix," the male voice intoned. "The crime occurred there. The Phoenix Police have to investigate this crime and they won't come to Tempe to take the report. You have to go to Phoenix to report the crime. Miss, do you understand?"

Barbara nodded and placed the telephone receiver back in its cradle.

"What did they say?" Mary Ann asked.

"You won't believe it. They can't take the report."

"What do you mean?"

"They said it happened in Phoenix, so I have to report it to the police from there, from my home. I guess it makes sense.

The two women stepped out into the cold night air. Mary Ann walked Barbara to her car and gave her a long hug. "Barbie, you be sure to call me when you get home."

"I will. I just can't believe it. I want them to look for the guy now, not after I call them from home. He'll get away with it".

Barbara McDaniel drove to her home at 1343 East Belleview Street in Phoenix. Then she called the Phoenix Police. Officer Tom Ezell came to Barbara's home at 10:02 p.m. and completed a police report. The report title was armed robbery because it was the most serious offense. The other offenses—assault, kidnapping, and attempted rape—were included in the body of the report.

FIVE

DETECTIVE ROBERT KORNEGAY settled his big frame behind his desk in the Crimes Against Persons Detail area of Phoenix Police Headquarters. He sipped black coffee and reviewed the robbery reports assigned to him from the night before. One of the reports named the victim as Barbara Sue McDaniel.

Later that day, Kornegay drove an unmarked car to the Western Parking Lot at 2nd Street and Fillmore where the crime took place. He walked the lot, treating it like a crime scene, but found no evidence that would lead to a suspect. He drove to the alley between 1st and 2nd streets and between McKinley and Pierce streets. He walked the alley's length north and south, looking for any possible physical evidence. He found tracks where a car had slid to a stop in the stones and saw tracks where a vehicle accelerated out of the alley and threw gravel from the alley on to Pierce Street. It helped to confirm Barbara's story, but he saw nothing that would lead him to a suspect.

Kornegay canvassed the area, beginning with the east side of the alley. He knocked on the front door of 710 North 2nd Street, presented his credentials, and talked to the owner, a Mr. Perko.

"Mr. Perko, did you or anyone that lives with you see or hear anything in the alley behind your house last night?"

"Well, I live alone, Detective, and last night, I didn't see anything. I went out about seven o'clock, just after supper, and I didn't come home until after the bars closed at one a.m."

"Thank you, sir," Kornegay said. He handed Perko a business card. "If you hear anything from your neighbors, feel free to call me or have them call me."

"Okay, Detective, I will."

Kornegay kept working 2nd Street, knocking on doors. He left his business card when no one answered and wrote those addresses in his notepad.

He crossed the alley and looked for windows and doors at the back of the shops that ran along 1st Street. He reasoned that one of their employees might have seen something through a window or an open door.

After he had left his business card on the door of a corner store, he walked into the Phoenix Credit Bureau at 705 North 1st Street and asked a woman at the front counter if he could talk to the office manager.

The manager, C. W. Nielson, came to the counter, and Kornegay presented his credentials.

"Mr. Nielson, I'd like to talk to you in private about a police matter."

"Sure, Detective, come into my office." Mr. Neilson swung open the half-size swinging gate attached to the front desk. Kornegay walked through the opening and the two men continued to Neilsen's office near the back of the building.

"I'd like to talk to your employees about an attack on a woman last night. It occurred in the alley behind your business. The suspect is a Mexican male, five-foot- eleven inches, wearing a tan jacket and tan pants. He had dark hair and a neat appearance except for a four- or five-day growth of beard—and possibly a moustache as well."

"I wasn't here myself," Neilson said. "I left just after five o'clock. You can talk to the ladies that work for me if you would like. In fact, it'll probably make 'em feel better if you explain in some detail what happened, and what they can do to prevent it from happening to one of them."

"Did anyone work past five o'clock last night?"

"That'd be the night crew. They're all men. I can check with them and see if they saw or heard anything, but they should've left by nine o'clock."

"Here's my business card. Please give me a call with any information they may give you."

"Whatever I can do to help, Detective. Can I introduce you to my clerks?"

Nielson walked Detective Kornegay out to the front desk and introduced him to an attractive blonde who looked to be her late twenties. "This is Mrs. Sandy Coe. In fact, she had a minor incident with a man last night while she was walking home. Mrs. Coe, would you tell Detective—Kor-ne-gay, was it?"

"Yes, Kornegay."

"Tell him all about it. I've got to get back to work."

Kornegay thanked Nielson and pulled out his notebook. Sandy Coe started telling her story.

"I clocked out at just after five o'clock and left the office. I started walking home and I heard a man whistle at me. He was in a car..."

Mrs. Coe described the white man in the blue car. When she finished, Kornegay had a few questions.

"Do you remember anything else about him?"

"No, that's all I can remember."

"Have any of you other ladies had any incidents with men in or around the credit bureau?"

"I can tell you about the transient that came in last night, Detective," Celia Padilla said.

"Please do," said Kornegay.

"It was just before five p.m. We were all getting ready to go home. Uh, me, Ruth Mercy, Elaine Edwards, and Darleen Giest. Well, this little man, maybe five foot tall, wobbled in, pushing his way through the wood front doors. We all just looked at him. Then he folded his arms and leaned on the front counter. He stared at the counter top like he was trying to focus on the design. He stared at the little black and white boomerangs in the gray Formica there. He was breathing heavily. The odor of alcohol came at me across the counter. It was terrible. I finally got him to say his name and where he lived. He was Eddie Peralta and lived at 3354 East Madison.

His clothes looked like they had been slept in, and the smell of whatever he had laid in was still on him. Yuk!"

Kornegay listened while the woman continued on about a drunk who'd staggered in the day before, bummed a cigarette, and left. The story, unfortunately, had little to do with any of the attempted rapes in the area.

Detective Kornegay explained to the clerks that a few blocks away on the night before a young man had forced himself into a woman's car and drove her to the alley behind the Credit Bureau. Kornegay said he believed the crime was sexually motivated, that the suspect fully intended to rape the woman. Kornegay then told the ladies how to keep themselves safe when going to or from work whether on foot or in their vehicles. He left them his business card and told them to call if they had additional questions or further information.

WHEN HE RETURNED to police headquarters, Kornegay mulled over the information he had gathered in the area of 2nd Street and Fillmore. Then he went over to the R & I Bureau. The clerk there found that an Edward M. Peralta, of 3354 East Madison, had reported a hit-and-run accident on August 8, 1959. There were no additional records or warrants on him. Kornegay wrote a supplement to the armed robbery report on Barbara McDaniel, adding the information he had obtained. Finally he reviewed his other assigned cases for similarities in the MO and went home.

PHOENIX POLICE DETECTIVE Larry Debus was assigned to the Crimes Against Persons Assaults Detail and was taking his turn in the rotation working second shift as a night detective. He reviewed his assigned reports and contacted victims to obtain further information. He found that a victim in one of Kornegay's cases said she could identify a suspect. He telephoned that victim, Barbara Sue McDaniel, and made an appointment for her to meet him at police headquarters at 5:30 that evening.

When Barbara arrived, officers took her to Detective Debus.

"I have the report number written down," Barbara told Debus. "Officer Ezell made the report last night. I was in Tempe when I called the police and they made me go to my apartment and call the Phoenix Police. I signed the report last night for Officer Ezell, report number 62-40126, armed robbery."

"Yes, ma'am," Debus said. "If the crime occurred in Phoenix we'll certainly take the report. The problem is bad guys don't understand we have beat areas, precinct boundaries, and city borders. Come with me over here to Interview Room Two where we can talk."

Barbara McDaniel told her story a second time to Detective Debus.

"I couldn't believe it when he was at my window, then he was inside my car, shoving me over. He kept pawing me. My father is going to kill this man when you find him."

"Miss McDaniel, can you remember any more details about the suspect that was not in your original police report?"

"Well, he was definitely a Mexican male, but he spoke very clearly without an accent."

"What about his description?"

"His beard was as if he hadn't shaved in four or five days."

"Did you smell the odor of alcohol on his breath at all?" Debus asked.

"No, I couldn't smell any alcohol, just cigarettes."

"Are you willing to press charges and appear in court?"

"Yes, I am. I gave my work and home telephone numbers to Officer Ezell."

"Would you be able to recognize the man if you saw him again?"

"Yes, I will never forget his face. And some of the things he said to me."

Debus had Barbara McDaniel view numerous photographs of Mexican male sex offenders from the known offender books in the detective bureau and from the R & I Bureau. She looked at each photograph carefully. "The man who did this to me is not in these pictures, Detective. Do you have any more that I could look at?"

"No ma'am, we don't." Debus said. "Now, we'll be looking to file kidnapping charges on this man because he restricted your movement and moved you from one place to another. And we'll file assault charges for touching you. And, as for using a knife and taking your money, of course that's armed robbery."

THE NEXT DAY Detective Kornegay reviewed the supplements to the Barbara McDaniel's case. He found the elements of the crime of armed robbery were present but felt the suspect didn't intend to rob the victim until he failed to carry out a rape. Therefore, he wrote:

> *Since the force and fear of force used by the suspect in this offense were done so with the intent of committing a crime of rape, this report should be unfounded as an armed robbery and reclassified as an attempted rape.*

The case was then reclassified and reassigned to an Assaults detective in the Crimes Against Persons Detail. Since Detective Debus was already familiar with this case, it was added to his caseload.

Debus reviewed numerous unsolved sexual assault cases. He compared Barbara McDaniel's suspect description and the MO to those in similar reports with similar suspect descriptions and MOs. He found a resemblance in nine unsolved sexual assault reports. Debus created a flyer with the suspect's description and had it placed in the police department's newsletter, the *Daily Bulletin*, for November 29, 1962.

By December 5th, Detective Debus had obtained photographs of possible suspects and completed photographic lineups with the victims in three of the nine Departmental Report Logs, or DR logs. He reviewed the reports and came up with five suspects who were brought in for a live lineup.

None of the victims were able to identify any of the suspects in the lineup as the suspect in their reports. Without witness identification in the lineup or evidence to link a suspect to the crimes, the cases were placed in pending status, meaning that these cases would not be actively worked unless further information was brought forward. If no information came forward, they would eventually become cold cases.

SIX

JUST AFTER 7:30 p.m. on Friday, February 22, 1963, Ernest Miranda left his home in Mesa and took another trip to downtown Phoenix, returning to the area near the Paramount Theater where he had encountered Barbara McDaniel in November.

On this evening, many people were attending films at the Paramount. The first show had let out when Ernie found a parking space on 2nd Avenue south of Adams Street.

He wore his olive green Army jacket and black pants. It was only fifty-nine degrees that night. The winter months were the only time he could wear the jacket in Arizona. January had been exceptionally cold and temperatures had dipped to thirty-nine degrees. Ernie was glad he had kept the jacket after his dishonorable discharge from the Army. The jacket was the only good thing the Army ever gave him.

Ernie thought his neatly combed back hair and clean, just-out-of-the-military appearance would allow him to blend in with the moviegoers. He combed the area for women walking alone north of Adams from 5th Avenue to 3rd Street. Tonight the women were walking in groups of three or more. He made his way back to the Paramount Theater.

He stood outside the Paramount's Adams Street side stage entrance and lit a cigarette. At about 8:30 p.m. he saw a woman leave the telephone office across Adams. She was alone, young, and attractive. He watched her walk westbound. He took a drag from his cigarette and blew a cloud of smoke into the cool night wind. He moved down his side of the street, paralleling the potential victim. His hands deep in his jacket pockets, cigarette dangling from his lips, he watched the young woman continue west across 3rd Avenue.

When Ernie previously followed telephone operators, he found that most of them parked at the Barns Parking Lot on the southwest corner of 4th Avenue and Monroe Street. He stopped at the corner of 3rd Avenue and threw his cigarette butt on the sidewalk. He was certain she was headed to the Barns lot. He crossed Adams and continued north on 3rd. *If I hurry, I can get to her car before she does.*

SYLVIA McLEOD FELT a little unsettled. Usually her friends walked with her for two blocks to her car. This evening the other girls were working different shifts, and she knew she would have to pay more attention when she walked alone.

Sylvia looked up the street toward the Barns lot. Her brand new Volkswagen Beetle really stood out. She thought it was so cute and it fit her personality so well. She was eighteen and thankful for her job as a telephone operator, fortunate to have a mature voice.

Sylvia crossed 4th Avenue at Monroe Street. She didn't see anyone around when she reached the parking area. Then she saw a man in the Barns Parking Lot walking in her direction. He had longer hair, combed back. He wore glasses and an Army jacket. He climbed into the car next to her blue Volkswagen. She relaxed when he got into the other car. She went to the driver's side of her car, opened the door, and slid into the driver's seat. She pulled the door shut. Now she felt safe. She got her keys out of her purse.

She heard her driver-side door open. It was the man in the Army jacket. A click sounded and then she felt something against her left shoulder. She looked to see a knife in the man's hand. She saw a black tattoo with the initials E.M. in the web of his hand. Then her eyes focused on the knife blade pressing against her shoulder. She looked through the man's horn-rimmed glasses and into his vacant eyes.

"Give me your money."

Sylvia thought fast. "I don't have any money."

"Are you sure?"

"I won't have any money until payday—that's next Friday." She kept her breathing even and tried not to show any fear.

"I'll take the car then," said Ernie. "Move over." He tried to force his way into the driver's seat, pushing his right hip against Sylvia's body.

"Not my new car," she shouted.

The Volkswagen's long stick shift, mounted on the floor between the seats, prevented Sylvia from moving. She was wedged in. She screamed.

Ernie looked up and saw headlights shining on him from a car driving down Monroe Street.

"Okay, okay," Ernie said. He backed up and raised his hands as if to surrender. "I will leave you alone." Ernie walked away quickly heading east on Monroe Street.

Sylvia pushed in the clutch and tried to start her car. Her hands trembled as she tried to put the key in the ignition. Tears rolled down her cheeks. The car came to life. She put the gearshift into reverse and shot out of the parking space. She ground the gears going into first and drove recklessly out of the parking lot onto 4th Avenue. She shifted into second as she crossed Monroe Street, then raced toward Van Buren. She accelerated, rolling through the stop sign, and turned right on Van Buren. She pulled into a Shell service station at the northwest corner of 3rd Avenue and Van Buren. Sylvia jerked the car to a stop, jumped out, and ran to the attendant.

"A man just tried to steal my car."

"Where is he?" the attendant asked.

"He had a knife. He ran when I screamed. I think he walked that way." Sylvia ran to the street corner. The attendant followed. She pointed toward 4th Avenue.

"I don't see him now."

"Come on, you gotta call the police, Miss." They ran back to the service station office and called the Phoenix Police.

Officer W. O. Simmons responded. He kept his voice low and slow, helping to calm Sylvia enough to tell him what happened. Simmons obtained the basic information and put out a description of the suspect for units in the area.

The dispatcher repeated the information, "All units be on the lookout for a Mexican male, combed-back black hair, green Army jacket, and black horn-rimmed glasses, armed with a knife. Last seen on foot, on Monroe Street, walking eastbound from 4th Avenue. Suspect is wanted for attempt—armed robbery."

Simmons notified his supervisor of the attempt–armed robbery and asked the radio dispatcher to send a Records and Information Bureau officer to lift prints from the victim's vehicle. R & I Bureau Officer Joe Garcia arrived a few minutes later and dusted the Volkswagen for fingerprints. He lifted latent prints from the outside of the driver-side door and from the top of the door frame.

Simmons's sergeant contacted the night desk sergeant who located a detective on rotation working nights and sent Detective Don Procunier to the Shell station. Procunier gathered details of the crime, went back to police headquarters, and located photos from the R & I Bureau of known suspects with similar MO's. A mug shot of one Ernest Arturo Miranda, who was as yet unknown to the Phoenix PD, was not among them. Procunier then returned to the Shell station to show the photographs to Sylvia McLeod.

Sylvia held the four 2x3-inch photographs in her hands under the bright light of the Shell station, looking intently at each one. She flipped through the four photographs twice.

"If you put glasses and a mustache on this one, it's the guy." She handed the photo of number three, labeled PPD #C-4009, back to Detective Procunier.

"Miss McLeod, are you sure?" the detective asked. "You see, I know this man, and he doesn't have a moustache and he doesn't wear glasses."

"Well I'm pretty sure it's him, anyway, but I would have to see him in person to be positive."

SEVEN

MARCH 7TH, 1963, Detective Carroll Cooley knocked on the wooden door of Sergeant Earl Moore's office, a door with a fogged glass pane emblazoned with gold and black block letters that read: DEPARTMENT POLYGRAPHER. Cooley had been working his other cases, and now he was back to Margaret Fair. He wondered if the polygraph was the right tool to use for the job.

"Hey, Sarge, I've got a rape case I'd like to run by you."

Sergeant Moore stopped writing and looked up at Cooley. "What do you have?" Moore reached across his desk blotter and pushed a button, switching off the fluorescent light on his metal desk lamp. He took his glasses off, and his oak desk chair squeaked as he leaned back. Moore pinched the bridge of his nose with his thumb and forefinger, squeezed his eyes shut, and opened them again.

"An eighteen-year-old victim who's shy and naive," Cooley said. "I need to know if she's telling the truth about a rape. She may have been with a boyfriend that night—"

"And," Moore interrupted, "she might've made a police report so she wouldn't get in trouble."

"That's right," Cooley said. "She told Young and Smith she would submit to a polygraph if requested to do so."

"I happen to have some time this morning if you want me to

interview her and put her on the polygraph."

"I'd really appreciate it, Sarge."

COOLEY TELEPHONED SUSANNE Williamson, Margaret Fair's sister, to confirm that Margaret could do another interview. Cooley and Moore drove to East Citrus Way. After introductions, everyone settled into a seat.

"Margaret, if you remember," Sergeant Moore said, "I believe you told detectives Young and Smith you would consent to a polygraph—a lie detector test—if requested to do so."

Maggie looked down at her hands. "Yeah," she said in a low voice. "I said I would if I had to."

Sue Williamson jumped in. "This polygraph—can you tell me what it is and how intrusive would it be for Maggie?"

"Sure. Simply, a polygraph measures and records several physiological indices such as changes in blood volume, pulse, respiration, and skin conductivity while the subject is asked a series of questions. The instrument will record the responses. Deceptive responses will produce physiological responses that can be differentiated from non-deceptive responses."

"You make it sound more like a doctor's examination, Sergeant," Sue said. "What will you be doing to Maggie to record the answers?"

"Well, we have several measures that we use in order to record blood volume, pulse, respiration, that sort of thing. She'll probably be a little nervous, but that's to be expected."

Sue turned to her sister. "You have to do this to show you're telling the truth, Maggie."

"I am telling the truth," Maggie said.

Maggie stood up, turned her back, and silently left the room. After a few long minutes, she returned, stopped in the middle of the room, frowning. "I don't want to do this."

Sue knew that look. "I know, sweetie, but this has to be done." Sue squared herself in front of Maggie and put her hands firmly on her sister's shoulders. "I know you're telling the truth...and this test will prove to the police that you are."

Maggie looked longingly back at the house as she followed

Cooley and Moore to the car. Cooley opened the car door and she slid into the backseat.

COOLEY, MOORE, AND Maggie entered Phoenix Police headquarters through the doors under the staircase on the west side of City Hall. Everything seemed to be the same as the last time, Maggie thought, except this time, the coffee smelled burnt. Maggie glanced at the interview room as they crossed the bureau floor to Sergeant Moore's office. There, Cooley introduced Maggie to Edna Hurt, the policewoman who would assist with the polygraph examination.

"Margaret, I will leave you in the capable hands of Sergeant Moore and policewoman Hurt, "Cooley said. Then he went to brief Sergeant Nealis on the progress of his cases.

"Miss Fair, the intent of the polygraph is to determine if you are being completely truthful with the detectives," Moore said. "Do you understand?"

Maggie stood up straight. "Yes, I will be truthful," she said softly.

"Then there should be no problem."

"But what does it do, exactly?"

"First I would like you to sit in the chair here next to my desk. We can talk a little bit and I'll explain to you what the instrument does and how it works, okay?"

Maggie nodded and sat down in the blond oak chair next to the sergeant's matching desk. She wriggled a little to sit to the back of the seat her feet together, flat on the floor. She put her hands in her lap and looked down.

"First I'll need your basic information, Margaret. Let's start with your name, your address, and who you live with." Maggie nodded and cleared her throat. She began to speak in a soft voice. The sergeant jotted the information on the form and then asked Maggie a wide range of questions, mostly about her education.

"That takes care of the required forms. Now, I have three groups of questions I'll be asking you," the sergeant said. "I'll ask you these questions before we use the polygraph and then several more times while you're being monitored by the polygraph instrument. These questions begin with 'Is your name Margaret Ann Fair?'"

Moore finished the questions. "Now, let me explain to you what a polygraph is, so you won't be so nervous."

Maggie made several little nods.

"The polygraph measures and records several physiological indices such as blood volume changes, pulse, respiration, and skin conductivity, while I ask you a series of questions. To measure these things, we will connect tubes and wires to your body in specific locations. This will monitor your physiological activities." He lifted his head and peered at her through his glasses. "You do understand, don't you?"

"Uh, I guess so…"

"Okay, great—let's move you over to the chair by the instrument." The sergeant stepped over to a table and chair next to his desk. "Here you go, have a seat there and put your arms on the arm boards."

Maggie moved to the chair by the polygraph instrument. The chair itself resembled an electric chair from a horror movie Maggie had watched at the Paramount. She hesitated, then slid into the seat and looked down at the straight boards forming the arms of the chair.

"Okay, good," Moore said. "Miss Hurt, could you help us here?"

"Yes, Sergeant. Maggie you have to take your hands out of your lap and put them on the arms of the chair here, palms down…can you do that for me?"

Maggie uttered a soft, "Umm…okay."

"Margaret, look here on the table," Moore said. "This single strip of scrolling paper is going to move under these pins while I ask you the three groups of questions. The pins resting on the paper are writing pens. The pens will make marks on the paper as it scrolls. That's how I'll monitor and record your physiological activities, okay?"

Moore looked at Maggie for confirmation. Maggie was distracted, watching Hurt put something on her left upper arm.

"Margaret," Moore continued, "what Miss Hurt is doing there is putting a blood pressure cuff on your arm. The black tubing runs from the cuff, there," he said, pointing at the tube on the cuff and following it with his finger, "to the polygraph instrument, here. You see, as blood pumps through your arm it is carried by pressure from the heart pumping. The changes in pressure caused by the heart pumping displace the air in the tubes. The tubes are connected to a bellows. The bellows will then move one of the pens on the strip of scrolling paper. You can see how that would work, right?"

"I uh…yes, I guess," Maggie muttered. She looked around, wrenching her head from her arm with the cuff, to the instrument, and back. Her eyes widened.

"There, there, Maggie, everything's okay," Moore said. "You mustn't look so frightened. Here." He grabbed two black rubber tubes. "The next thing Miss Hurt is going to do is take these two rubber tubes and place one around your chest and one around your abdomen. This is how I'll record your respiratory rate."

Maggie squirmed in the chair. "Is this all necessary?"

"Just one more thing and then we can get started."

"What's the one more thing?"

"Galvanic skin resistance. It's a measure of the sweat on your fingertips. The fingertips are a good place to look for sweat." Moore believed he was calming Margaret down with his explanations and expertise. "The idea is that we sweat more when we are placed under stress. Fingerplates, called "galvanometers," are attached to two of your fingers. These plates measure the skin's ability to conduct electricity. When the skin is sweaty it conducts electricity much more easily than when it is dry, you see?"

"Will the electricity on my sweaty fingers give me a shock?"

"No, Margaret. Look here. See, this finger clip is to record your sweat from your third finger and this clip on your index finger is for your sweat there. Okay?"

"Margaret, look at me," Miss Hurt said. "You'll have to sit very still so the sergeant can get accurate readings. Do you understand?"

Maggie nodded slowly and swallowed.

"All right," Moore said. He took a seat at the table where the polygraph instrument rested. Maggie watched a red light come on when he flipped a toggle switch. He flipped another toggle switch and then another. Several pins moved on the paper as it started scrolling. "Everything seems to be in working order. Margaret, you'll have to relax in order for me to get good readings. Do you understand?"

Maggie sat in the chair and looked down. Her back was straight against the back of the chair, her arms resting flat on the horizontal boards. One long rubber tube ran across her chest and another one looped across her stomach. The blood pressure cuff squeezed her upper left arm, and clips with wires ran from two of her fingers. She thought that the only thing missing was a helmet with electrodes like in the Frankenstein movie that had played at the theater.

"I guess so," Maggie said, hoping there would be nothing else required of her.

"I'm looking for the amount of fluctuation in your physiological activities. So all you have to do is calmly answer the questions. Answer yes or no, whichever is a truthful answer to the question.

Moore stopped and looked at Maggie over the top of the instrument. "Margaret, I know you're shy and quiet, but please answer yes or no rather firmly, okay?"

"Yes," Maggie said firmly.

Moore conducted a stimulation test where he asked a question known by the person being polygraphed to be true. He would then ask them to answer falsely.

"Margaret, I need you to answer falsely to a question. I want you to deliberately lie. I would like you to say 'no' when I ask you if Susanne Williamson is your sister."

"I'll try." Maggie took a quick breath through her nose and blew it out her mouth. She sat up straight, blinked a few times, and swallowed hard.

"Is your sister's name Susanne Williamson?"

"No," Maggie said.

The pins jumped across the paper. "Okay," the sergeant said, "that's what it looks like when you lie."

Moore began by asking Maggie the three sets of questions he had previously asked her in the interview portion of the test. The examination took two hours.

Edna Hurt disconnected an exhausted Maggie from the

instrument, and the two of them took a walk to get a cold beverage. Sergeant Moore wrote his report. Then he went looking for Detective Cooley.

"Carroll, I'd like talk to you about Margaret's polygraph results in private," Moore said, when he had found Cooley's desk. Cooley ground out a cigarette and took a breath mint from the roll in his pocket. The two men went to Moore's office and closed the door. The sergeant took a seat behind his oak desk. The chair squeaked as he settled in.

"Well, Sarge, how'd it go?" Cooley asked, shifting the mint in his mouth.

"I have three main problems. First, it appears that Margaret Ann has a low IQ. She had difficulty comprehending the examination. Edna assisted me, and she too feels that Margaret Ann is mentally slow."

Cooley nodded and waited for Sergeant Moore to continue.

"Secondly, Margaret Ann is very withdrawn and very shy, as you know. She told me she had difficulty with her school classes. She said she finally quit school the early part of this year after entering the eleventh grade at Phoenix Union."

Cooley responded with another nod. His expression showed concern.

"Third, one of the questions on the form is in reference to when Margaret had her last menstrual cycle. She had just begun her menstrual cycle, and I think she may have taken something for the cramps."

"Okay," Cooley said. "So what does all this mean?"

"It means that any one of these factors can affect the polygraph. But all of these factors together made the test very difficult," Moore said, shaking his head.

"So what's your final conclusion, Sarge? Is she telling the truth?"

"That's just it. The inconsistencies I mentioned made the analysis too difficult. I'm unable to reach a conclusion."

"Okay, then, what do we do, when you can't reach a conclusion?"

"Well, I would like to give Margaret Ann another polygraph

examination in about a week."

"I really thought the polygraph would shed some light on the investigation Sarge. I've spent a considerable amount of time on this case and now this puts me back at square one."

CARROLL COOLEY STARTED the detective car and drove north on 7th Street. Sergeant Moore sat beside him. They were taking Maggie home. Cooley turned the Plymouth east onto Marlette and eased off the accelerator.

"Margaret, could you point out the exact location where you were abducted?" Cooley asked.

"Umm, yes," Maggie said softly.

"Tell me where to stop the car."

"Stop here."

Cooley pulled to the curb in front of an apartment building at 777 East Marlette. Maggie looked across the street and pointed through the open window. "This is the place. The man's car was parked over there."

Cooley got out of the car and inspected the location. He walked across Marlette and looked for anything that might link a vehicle or a suspect to this crime scene. Then he walked fifty yards down the street in each direction. He saw there were no streetlights on Marlette and the trees were nearly leafless. He was disappointed but not surprised that he didn't find anything of evidentiary value.

COOLEY STOOD JUST inside the front door of the Williamson residence. Sergeant Moore took a seat on the chair across from Maggie and her sister. Moore explained the reasons he believed the polygraph results were inconclusive.

"My sister's not a liar, Sergeant," Sue said, "and your department has put her through heck."

"I'm sorry, Mrs. Williamson. There are several reasons the polygraph was inconclusive."

Sue stood up. "What are we supposed to do?"

"Well, to clear up some of the issues, Margaret Ann would probably have to take another polygraph examination. I would suggest in a week or so."

"I'll show you gentlemen out," Sue said. She marched across the living room and opened the front door. The two men left. Sue stood there, at attention, chin up, until the car made the turn from the cul-de-sac onto 10th Street. Then she slammed the door.

COOLEY DROVE SERGEANT Moore to Phoenix Police headquarters, parked the car, and walked a block north on 2nd Avenue to the Paramount Theatre. He asked for an employee named Reginald Fertig.

Cooley waited for Fertig in the empty lobby, gazing at the walls while his shoes sank into the plush carpet. The elaborate Spanish baroque decor took him back in time. He couldn't recall when the theater was last called the Orpheum. He remembered it had been built in 1928 or '29, along with several other downtown buildings, including City Hall, where the police department was housed.

Twenty-one-year-old Reginald Fertig appeared from behind a heavy, red velour curtain hanging at one end of the lobby. He extended a hand, palm up, and greeted the detective. Cooley noticed that Reginald stood with perfect posture. He looked exceptionally neat in his pressed usher's uniform, and his shoes were polished to a high gloss.

"You must be Detective Cooley," Reginald said.

"I'd like to talk to you about Margaret Fair," Cooley said.

"What would you like to know, Detective?"

"I understand the two of you have a relationship."

"Yes sir, we have a great working relationship and we're bus buddies."

"Bus buddies—what does that mean?"

"We ride the bus to and from work together. Well, sometimes I drive my car, but either way, we share the ride."

"Reginald, could you tell me what happened when the two of you rode the bus last Saturday night? That would have been March second." Cooley pulled his pad of paper from his jacket pocket and flipped it open to a blank page.

"Sure, Detective, we left the theater around eleven-thirty that night and caught the bus at about eleven forty-five. We sat together in a seat near the front of the bus on the right side, if you're facing forward."

"At any time did you notice anyone or any suspicious vehicle at any of the bus stops or along the bus route?"

"No sir. We just sat and talked and minded our own business."

"Do you have any interest in Miss Fair?"

Reginald hesitated before he spoke. "No sir, I'm not interested in girls. In fact I could do without them."

"Thank you, sir." Cooley put away his notepad. "Here's my business card. Should you think of anything else that may be helpful, please give me a call."

"I certainly will, Detective." Reginald turned and disappeared behind the red curtain.

AT PHOENIX POLICE headquarters, Cooley began searching the sergeant's DR logs. He looked for rape cases and attempted rapes reported in the area of 7th Street and Marlette. He found none. He then sought assistance from the R & I Bureau at police headquarters in order to research cases with a similar MO. He widened the search by increasing the area of city blocks. Still he found no other rape reports. He further broadened his search to include rapes and attempted rapes that had occurred in the previous six months. The R & I Bureau produced eleven reports. Two reports stood out. They had been assigned to Detective Larry Debus. Both cases were attempted rape and robbery.

These crimes had not been committed in the Marlette Street area. They had occurred in the downtown area of Phoenix near the Paramount Theatre. The victims were Barbara Sue McDaniel and Sylvia McLeod.

EIGHT

PAUL HENKLE HAD not yet found employment after being honorably discharged from the United States Marine Corps. He took a drag from his cigarette as he stood under the overhang outside the ballet school at 7th Street and Marlette Avenue.

That cool March night in Phoenix Paul kept in mind it was exactly one week since his sister-in-law's sister Maggie had been attacked. The waiting reminded him of guard duty at Camp Lejeune, only this was better. He was wearing civilian clothes, it wasn't raining, and his only job for now was making sure that Maggie got home safely after her bus ride from work.

Just before midnight, Paul field-stripped his second cigarette butt, twisting the filter off at the point where it met the tobacco, shredding the paper, and letting the unburned tobacco fall to the ground. He then peeled the paper away from the filter, discarded the paper, and shredded the filter. It was a ten-second process he had learned in the military.

A lone car drove slowly into the area. The vehicle was an older model and looked light green under the street lamp as it made a turn at the corner. The second time the car drove by, slowly, it turned east onto Marlette Avenue from 7th Street. The headlights shone on

Paul. He looked away and then looked back again. He blinked a few times and squinted, trying to adjust to the rapid changes in the light. He hoped to see the driver's face, but it was too dark inside the car. He got a license plate number: D-F-L-3-1-2. The car continued eastbound on Marlette and then turned south at 9th Place. Paul wanted a closer look at the car, but he couldn't leave his post. Maggie's bus would be arriving any minute.

At 12:10 a.m., the city bus ground to a stop at the corner of 7th Street and Marlette. The air brakes hissed, the doors folded open, and Maggie stepped off. After a few paces, she waved back at the driver and Reginald. Then she saw Paul walking toward her.

"How was work?" Paul asked.

"Oh, okay, I guess."

"Hey, uh, I don't want to scare you, but I saw a car driving around with a guy in it."

"You did?"

"Yeah. Uh, if you're not too afraid, maybe we can look for it."

"I'm not afraid when I'm with you," Maggie said softly, without making eye contact. They walked east on Marlette for two blocks.

Paul pointed south. "I saw it go this way. It turned here on Ninth Place."

They walked south on 9th Place past Claremont Street. "There's a car parked down on Rose Lane," Paul whispered to Maggie. They crouched a little and kept walking. "Did the guy's car look like that one?"

Maggie looked at the car in the darkness, but she didn't answer. They tiptoed closer toward the car.

"It looks like the same car," Maggie whispered. "It's the same color…but cars look too much alike to me."

"Stay here." Paul walked quickly but quietly toward the car. He wanted to get a look at the driver, the only occupant. The car roared to life, the headlights came on, and the tires squealed as it lurched from the curb and sped eastbound on Rose Lane. Paul ran after it for fifty yards until he had to stop. Out of breath, he inhaled the smell of burnt rubber and gas fumes. He walked back to where Maggie waited for him.

"Could you see him?" Maggie asked. "Could you see the man?"

"No," Paul said, breathing hard. "But for sure the license plate is from Arizona, and I got the number earlier. Let's get you home."

AT 2:00 A.M., an excited Paul Henkle was still awake. He couldn't wait until morning to call the number for Detective Cooley. *They're open all night, and I can't sleep anyway.* The front desk officer, Dave Anderson, took the call and made notes when Paul Henkle called in.

"Detective Cooley said to drop a dime if I saw anything suspicious while walking with Miss Fair."

"Is that right?" Anderson asked.

"Well, this guy was circling the block around Seventh Street and Marlette. To me that was suspicious, then it parked at Ninth Place and Rose Lane. The vehicle was similar to the one used in a kidnap and rape a week ago on Marlette. When I went closer, to get a look at the driver, it tore off."

"Okay," Anderson said. "We appreciate the information."

"And one more thing," Paul said. "Could you tell Detective Cooley the license plate on the car was from Arizona? I think the number was DFL–312."

"Hold on for a minute, will ya, son?" Anderson put Paul on hold and contacted the Records and Information Bureau. They ran Henkle to see if he was a crackpot. Paul Wayne Henkle came back clean, no wants and no warrants. Then Anderson called the motor vehicle division with the license plate. After a few minutes Anderson told Paul the license plate was registered to a 1958 Oldsmobile sedan.

"No, sir, with all due respect, it's not an Oldsmobile. It was an older Packard. I'm sure of it."

"What did Miss Fair say about the car?" Anderson asked.

"She said it looked like the car because it was the same color, light green. But she also said she doesn't know cars, and they all look the same to her."

NEW REPORTS OF assaults and rapes from the weekend were added to the detectives' caseloads on Mondays. The day began with a cigarette, coffee, and a triage of in-boxes, prioritizing which cases would be worked first, based on a balance of organization and solvability.

The sergeant's DR log tracked the progress of each case from the time of the original report completed by the patrol officers. The supplemental reports that followed would be added to the log and passed on to the detective in charge of the case. Most of the cases would be solved. Those crimes committed by the same suspect would be tied together and several cases could be cleared. Some cases however would eventually become cold.

After a too-short weekend, Detective Cooley read the latest supplemental report to the Maggie Fair case on Monday, March 11. It was authored by Officer Anderson and contained the information provided by Paul Henkle.

Cooley asked Detective Wilfred "Bill" Young to go with him to 1014 East Citrus Way, to contact Paul Henkle in person. While enroute, the two men discussed the case.

"This could be a real lead," Cooley said.

"You never know, Carroll."

WHEN PAUL HENKLE told the detectives the whole story about the suspicious vehicle, they asked him why he thought the car was a Packard.

"I know the car was a Packard Patrician 'cause I had a buddy who owned one just like it. It had the same oblong taillights that ran along the quarter panel. And at night, they look like four taillights because of the chrome strip in the middle, but they're really just two lights."

Cooley asked Paul to accompany the detectives to the Otis Bacon Studebaker dealer at 3rd Avenue and Indian School Road where they found a 1953 Packard Patrician.

Paul pointed out the taillights. "This is just like it. The taillights are the very same as the ones as on the car I saw. In fact, the only thing I'm not sure about is the numbers on the license plate. I think I got the letters right, D–F–L, but the numbers might be one or two off. It was kind of dark and the car was driving away."

The detectives drove Paul back to the house on Citrus Way. Mr. James Williamson, Sue's husband, wanted a word with the detectives in private. They walked out onto the driveway near the street.

"I might be able to explain Maggie's actions and clear up some of the confusion with her story."

"How's that, Mr. Williamson?" Cooley asked.

"I knew Maggie's story wouldn't sound too good. You see, Maggie is, well, very slow mentally. In fact, she had to quit high school after failing her junior year.

"Is that right?" Cooley said. "I noticed she was shy and quiet, and she doesn't make eye contact all the time, but she didn't seem slow to me."

"Well Maggie's very shy, hardly ever talks to men. In fact, she probably hasn't spoken thirty words to me in the last eleven years I've known her. She pretty much never speaks to me unless I talk first."

"Well, thank you, Mr. Williamson. We'll keep that in mind."

BACK AT POLICE headquarters, Cooley telephoned the motor vehicle division.

"I'd like you to run a registration check for me on all of the Arizona license plates that start with the letters D-F-L."

"You're kidding, right, Detective?" the clerk asked.

"No, no, ma'am," Cooley said. "I'm looking for an older Packard. Phonetically the letters are David–Frank–Lincoln, and the numbers may be close to 3-1-2. It could mean a lot to this sexual assault investigation I'm working. I appreciate whatever you can find out."

The clerk put Cooley on hold for several minutes, then came back on the phone. "I checked all of the license plates that started with D-F-L, registered to a Packard. The only one close was D-F-L-3-1-7. Do you have a pencil handy, Detective?"

"I do. Go ahead."

"Okay, David–Frank–Lincoln 3-1-7 is registered to a 1953 Packard four-door, to a Twila M. Hoffman at 210 North Le Baron Street, Mesa, Arizona."

"Thank you very much," Cooley said. He notified Sergeant Nealis of the progress in the case, updated his notes, and arranged to go to Mesa with Detective Young the following morning.

COOLEY and Young found the house at 210 North Le Baron Street vacant on the morning of March 12th. A man answered when Cooley knocked on the door to the neighboring house. The detectives showed their credentials and introduced themselves.

"Can you tell us anything about the people who lived next door?" Cooley asked, pointing at the vacant house.

"The folks who lived there moved out on Sunday, officers."

"This past Sunday?" Cooley asked.

"Yes, sir."

"Do you know their name?"

"Yes, sir, Ernest Miranda, he goes by Ernie."

"Can you tell me what he looked like?"

"He's a Mexican, about twenty-three years old, has a mustache and wears glasses with black frames. I think they call 'em horn-rimmed."

"Do you know a Twila Hoffman?" Young asked.

"Twila would be Ernie's wife. They also have three kids."

"Do you know where they moved to?" Cooley asked.

"Or where he works?" Young asked.

"I'm not sure where they moved too, but they had a moving truck from his work. Um, let me think…United Produce," the man said. "That was on the side of the truck."

THE DETECTIVES DROVE to the United Produce warehouse at 3rd and Madison streets. They went to the office and asked for the foreman.

"Does Ernest Miranda work for you?" Cooley asked.

"Yep. He works at night on the dock."

"He moved out of his house last weekend and might have used one of your trucks to move to the new place."

"Gave him permission myself, but I don't know where they moved to."

"You don't know where he moved too?"

"No, ah, he didn't say," the foreman said.

"Do you have a telephone number for him?" Cooley asked.

"No, he didn't give me his new phone number."

"Is there anything else you can tell us about Ernie?" Young asked.

"He's a hard worker. Wish I had more like him."

It was clear to the detectives that the foreman was covering for his dockworker and they wouldn't get more information from him. When an employee moved to another residence, they would at least give their employer a new telephone number to call them for work, and an address, for payroll purposes. Also Ernie may or may not have had permission to use the truck.

THE FOLLOWING MORNING, Wednesday, March 13, Cooley and Young stood in line at the United States Post Office at 522 North Central Avenue. The teller informed them that a change of address was on file for Ernest Arthur Miranda, who had moved from 210 North Le Baron, in Mesa, to 2525 West Mariposa Street in Phoenix.

The detectives returned to police headquarters. Cooley notified Sergeant Nealis of the new information. Young ran a check on Ernest Miranda's criminal history with the city of Mesa, the State of Arizona, and the federal prison system. He found that Ernesto Miranda was a Hispanic male, born March 9, 1941. He was now twenty-two years old, and he had a criminal history.

"Listen to this, Carroll," Young told Cooley, holding Miranda's rap sheet. "Miranda was first arrested in 1956, at age fifteen. He was charged with "assault with intent to commit rape" in Mesa. He was arrested in 1957, in Los Angeles, California, for robbery, at age sixteen. In 1959, at age eighteen, he moved to Tennessee, where he was arrested for auto theft and did a year in federal prison."

WHILE DRIVING TO the address on Mariposa, Cooley said to Young, "If this guy Miranda refuses to go downtown with us, there's not enough probable cause to arrest him."

"In that case," Young said, "we'll have to leave him at his house."

Cooley parked the detective car in the street. A light gray 1953 Packard four-door sat in the driveway. The Arizona license plate number read DFL-317. Cooley looked through the vehicle's backseat window and saw light-colored upholstery with a vertical pattern.

"Hey, Bill, look at this. The same interior as Margaret Fair described. And look what's tied across the back of the front seat."

"Isn't that what Maggie described as a rope handle?"

"Looks like it to me."

The detectives approached the front door of the house and knocked. A woman opened the door, holding a baby in her arms. The detectives presented their identification and introduced themselves. The woman said she was Twila Hoffman.

"Can we talk to Ernest Miranda?" Cooley asked.

"Ernie worked last night and he's still sleeping," Twila said. "I guess I can wake him up if you'd like."

The detectives nodded. "We'd appreciate it," Cooley said.

Twila closed the door and several minutes later Ernie emerged, wearing only khaki trousers and black rimmed glasses.

"What do you want?" Ernie asked.

"Are you Ernest Miranda?" Cooley said.

"Yeah."

"Well, we would like you to come down to Phoenix Police headquarters with us so we can talk."

"What's this about?" Ernie asked.

Cooley glanced over at Twila and the baby. "It concerns a police investigation. And we'd rather not discuss it here in front of your family."

"Okay. But I gotta get dressed first." Ernie turned and walked into the house, leaving the front door open. He looked back at the detectives and said, "Come on in."

Cooley and Young stood in the living room. A few minutes later Ernie joined them. He had added a white T-shirt, a belt, and a pair of shoes to his attire.

The three men walked out to the street. The detectives got into the front seat of their car and Ernie slid into the backseat and closed the door. At the time, Phoenix Police policy mandated that when a suspect is arrested and placed in a detective vehicle, the suspect will be handcuffed behind his back and a second officer/detective must ride in the backseat with the suspect. But Ernie was not handcuffed, and he'd not been placed under arrest. He was going downtown to talk to the detectives about an investigation.

It was a short drive from Mariposa Street to downtown Phoenix, and the conversation avoided any discussion of the crimes that were under investigation. During the small talk that ensued, Detective Young told Ernest Miranda, "You know, you don't have to talk to us if you don't want to."

NINE

COOLEY AND YOUNG escorted Ernest Miranda to the south entrance of police headquarters. They entered the building and proceeded left, past the booking desk and into the detective bureau. Cooley went to his desk and gathered his notes, along with the file on the Margaret Fair case. Young walked with Ernie over to Interview Room Two and opened the door.

"Miranda, have a seat. We'll be right with you."

When the door closed, Ernie walked around the worn, gray metal table and dragged a gray metal chair out from under it. He slid onto the seat and looked at his reflection in the mirrored door. Ernie's black horn-rimmed glasses dominated his face. He had a pug nose and full lips. His bull neck looked out of proportion to his thin torso. He no longer noticed the tattoos on his arms. His own image reminded him, although there was a family resemblance, that he was not like his father or his brothers. He put his elbows on the table, ducked his head, and ran his hands through his black hair from front to back. *I don't know which one this is about. I will just deny everything, admit to nothing, and make them prove it.*

YOUNG AND COOLEY went to Sergeant Nealis's office, where they updated him on the Margaret Fair rape case. Nealis was a good leader. Detectives didn't mind working for him, and they valued his input on cases. Cooley put a thick manila folder on the corner of the sergeant's desk.

The men lit cigarettes. Nealis took a drag, blew out the smoke, and said, "Okay, what do you have on this case?"

"We've got a guy who had access to a car that was possibly the same vehicle seen near the scene of a kidnapping," Cooley said.

"A full week after the crime," Young added.

"You're saying the suspect returned to scene of the crime," Nealis said.

"The license number given to us by the witness is close, but not exact," Cooley said.

"The color of the suspect vehicle given by the victim was light green, and Miranda's car is clearly white over gray," Young said.

"She got the interior right, including the rope across the back of the front seat," Cooley said.

"Miranda, the investigative lead, has a record, and he fits the general description of the suspect," Young added.

"We don't have enough probable cause to arrest him," Cooley said. "We need more evidence, and we'll need a confession."

"Well, start by getting a confession," Nealis said.

COOLEY AND YOUNG returned to Interview Room Two. Cooley glanced at the thick manila folder in his hand—Miranda's case file. Cooley took a deep breath and looked through the one-way mirror. Ernie sat with his arms folded across his chest. He leaned back in the metal chair, his legs stretched under the table, crossed at the ankles.

Cooley pulled a roll of Certs breath mints out of his suit coat pocket and extracted one from the roll with his teeth. He sucked on the breath mint and entered the interview room. Young followed behind him. Cooley placed the manila folder on the table and seated himself across the table from Ernie in one of the two metal chairs there. He checked his wristwatch and noted it was 10:30 a.m. The second metal chair scraped the floor as Young pulled it out and away from the table and sat in it. Cooley opened the manila folder and looked at the police report on top of the two inches of stacked papers.

"Ernest, Ernesto, or Ernie—how would like to be addressed?"

"Ernie's okay."

"Ernie, this first report is from Saturday night, March second, and it continues into Sunday morning, March third. About ten days ago a young woman was walking on Marlette Avenue near Seventh Street. A man picked her up in a car. She was taken into a desert area where she was raped and robbed. Then the man brought her back to Twelfth Street around Bethany Home or Rose Lane."

Ernie sucked his teeth. "What does this have to do with me?"

"Well," Cooley said, "your Packard, with license plate DFL-317, has been identified as the car used by the man who picked up the woman that night."

Ernie sat up in his chair, retracted his legs, and refolded his arms across his chest. "No, it couldn't have been me, because I work on Saturday nights. I was on the loading dock at United Produce. You can ask my wife, she saw me go to work."

"Look, Ernie," Cooley said, "you have a history of rape, robbery, and auto theft, for which you've been to prison. You're a Peeping Tom. You follow women to their cars in downtown Phoenix and, in this report," Cooley took a report from the folder and placed it on the table in front of Ernie. "You tried to get in this woman's car, you held her at knifepoint. You tried to take her car and get money from her. That was in February."

Ernie's eyes fixed on the report on the table. He shrugged with one shoulder.

"Before that, in this report," Cooley continued, as he put another report on the table, "last November you got in this woman's car with her and drove down an alley to rape her. She talked you out of raping her and you robbed her at knifepoint."

Cooley paused to let the information sink in. Ernie was fidgeting in his seat. He leaned forward and blurted, "I don't know what you're talking about...I swear to God I was at work on all of those nights."

"Ernie, look. There's a pattern of behavior in these crimes here. I have several reports in this folder. If a reasonable person were to read these reports, they would say it describes you and it describes your behavior. And, I have to say, your behavior's getting worse. I know you committed all of these crimes." Cooley paused. "In fact, I think you might be in need of psychiatric help."

"You got it wrong. I didn't do nothing to those women...I'm innocent. I ain't admitting to nothing."

"How about this, Ernie," Cooley said. "What if I have you stand in a line with, say, three other guys? Then I'll have some of the women in these reports come in and take a look at the four of you men standing there. It'll be you and three other men standing in a lineup."

Ernie looked at the table and shook his head from side to side and refolded his arms.

"If none of the women pick you out of the lineup as the man in these reports, I'll take you home. What do you say?"

Ernie scooted back in his chair. "I can do that. It'll prove it wasn't me."

Cooley stood, his chair scraping the floor. He picked up the manila folder, then he and Young left the room.

The interview had taken just over thirty minutes. By 11:15 a.m., Cooley had telephoned three of the victims in the reports: Margaret Fair, the victim of kidnapping, rape, and armed robbery of four dollars on March 3, 1963. Sylvia McLeod, the victim of attempted kidnapping and attempted armed robbery, February 22, 1963. Barbara McDaniel, the victim of kidnapping, attempted rape, and armed robbery of eight dollars on November 27, 1962.

Margaret Fair and Barbara McDaniel agreed to come to police headquarters. Sylvia McLeod hadn't answered her telephone when Cooley called.

DETECTIVE YOUNG TOOK the elevator to the fifth-floor jail and arranged for three Hispanic male inmates to stand in the live lineup. A jailer assisted with bringing the inmates to Interview Room Two where Ernie was waiting.

Cooley entered the interview room with four 8½X11-inch white cards. Each card had a large black number on it, numbered one through four. A string was attached to each card so they could be hung around the necks of the men in the lineup.

"You will be lined up with these three men. What number do you want to wear in the lineup?" Cooley laid the numbered cards on the table.

"I'll be number one, then," Ernie said, taking the card from the table and placing the string around his neck.

MARGARET Fair and Barbara McDaniel arrived at police headquarters just before 11:30 a.m. Officers kept them separate. Margaret was the first to stand outside of the closed door to Interview Room Two.

She looked through the one-way mirrored door at the men in the live lineup. She recalled being interviewed in this same room. She remembered the white walls and small holes in the acoustic ceiling tiles. Only this time it was different—she was outside looking in.

Cooley stood behind Maggie. "Look at the men there and let me know if any of them look familiar to you. If they do look familiar to you, tell me where you know them from."

"I understand," Maggie said softly. She wrung her hands, swallowed, and looked through the glass door. After a short period, she quietly said, "I think number one looks like the man, but I'm not positive. I mean he's the same size and has the same facial features as the man did. If I could hear him talk, I might know him by his voice." Maggie then moved away from the door.

Barbara McDaniel had been waiting with Detective Young in the detectives' area. She now moved up and stood outside the mirrored door to the interview room. Young stepped back. Cooley stood behind Barbara and said, "Look into the room at the men there and let me know if any of them look familiar to you. If they do look familiar, tell me where you know them from."

Barbara looked through the glass for a long time. "The number-one man looks like the same man who robbed and tried to rape me, but I'm not positively sure."

Young took the victims back to the detectives' area while Cooley had the live lineup photographed. The prisoners were then escorted back to the jail, out of view of the victims. Ernie remained in the interview room. Detective Cooley spoke to Maggie and

Barbara, asking them to stay at the police station in case he needed them again after he re-interviewed the suspect. They both said they would.

THE DETECTIVES LIT cigarettes and talked into the sergeant's office, where they could talk in private.

"What do want to do, Carroll?" Young asked. "This lineup was gonna put him away, but the girls aren't positive."

"Well, this certainly is disheartening," Cooley said. "I guess I'll just have to talk to him."

Cooley finished his cigarette, extracted another breath mint, and reentered the interview room with the manila folder. Young followed and took a seat. Cooley remained standing and placed the thick folder on the table.

Ernie noticed Cooley's grim look. *This could only mean bad news for me.* "How did I do?" Ernie asked.

Cooley sighed and sadly shook his head. "Not too good, Ernie."

Ernie's eyes widened, shocked. "They identified me, then?"

"Yes, Ernie, they did."

"Well," Ernie looked at his hands interlaced on the table and said slowly, "I guess I'd better tell you about it then."

"Yes, Ernie, I think you should."

Cooley sat down and opened the manila folder. He removed a notepad and the Margaret Fair rape case file. "Seventh Street and Marlette, Saturday, March second. What happened?"

Ernie sat up in his chair and put his elbows on the table in front of him.

"I was driving around in northeast Phoenix when I saw the woman walking alone down a dark street. I pulled up and stopped just ahead of her and got out of the car. When she came close enough, I told her, 'Don't make any noise, I won't hurt you, get in the car.' She got in the backseat without any trouble. I had a small rope inside the car and I tied her ankles and wrists with the rope. Then I got in the front seat and drove a few miles into the desert." Ernie licked his lips and continued. "I pulled up to the side of the road. By this time the girl was untied. I got into the backseat and said I wouldn't hurt her. Then I told her to take her clothes off and she said, 'Take me home.' She wouldn't take off her clothes, so I took off all her clothes."

Cooley looked up from his note-taking. "Then what happened?"

"She begged me not to do it." Ernie swallowed. "She said she had never been with a boy before. I tried anyway and couldn't do it. I tried again and could only get a small bit in, about a half inch of my penis."

"Did you reach climax?" Cooley asked.

"Yeah, but I don't think it got inside her. Could have."

"Then what'd you do, Ernie?"

"Then I told her to put her clothes on and she did. Then I asked where she lived and she said Tenth Street and something. I can't remember. I drove back to where I picked her up and let her off around Tenth or Twelfth Street." Ernie sucked his teeth again. "She told me, 'This ain't where I live.' I told her to go ahead and get out, this is as far as I'm taking you. Then I asked her if she would pray for me. Oh, and I told her I needed some money. She opened her wallet or purse and gave me four dollars. I took the money and left."

Cooley quietly wrote for a minute. Ernie sat in the silence, broken only by the scratch of Cooley's pencil on his notepad. Ernie exhaled and looked at the table. His shoulders were slumped and his hands lay palms-down in his lap.

Ernie wasn't telling the whole truth. Cooley knew suspects rarely told the whole truth. You have what the victim reports to the police, what the evidence yields, and what the suspects will admit to you. These puzzle pieces have overlapping areas that represent the truth. Enough of each piece combined together and the puzzle is solvable, sometimes prosecutable. But rarely do you ever get the whole truth.

Cooley thought Ernie had given him enough puzzle pieces on the Maggie Fair case to prosecute him. He asked Ernie about the Barbara Sue McDaniel case.

"Ernie, you've also been identified by another young woman who was robbed at knifepoint. She says you tried to rape her. It was back on November twenty-seventh of last year."

"Yeah. I remember. I shoved her over in her car and got in. She screamed. I put my hand over her mouth and told her to shut up." Ernie licked his lips and swallowed. "Told her she wouldn't be hurt. Then I drove her car into an alley and stopped the car. I was gonna rape her, but she talked me out of it. So I just took her money."

The victims had each reported that the suspect held them at knifepoint. "Did you use a knife to rob these women, Ernie?"

Ernie had been through the penal system and knew that armed robbery with a knife would mean more jail time than if he had used a lesser instrument. He said, "It was only a fingernail file. I held it up in my sleeve. It might have looked like a knife. I pressed the point against the one woman's side when she got in her car."

Cooley pulled out the police report listing Sylvia McLeod as the victim. "Do you remember the woman in the Barns Parking Lot? She drove a new Volkswagen Beetle. The car was blue."

"I remember that one," Ernie said, "but nothing happened with that one. I ran off."

"The woman saw your knife and described the tattoo on the hand you held the knife in—E.M. The tattoo read just like the E.M. right there on the web of your right hand."

Ernie looked at the E.M. tattooed in the web of his right hand and covered it with his left hand.

Ernie then put his hand over his mouth. "I used a fingernail file that looked like a knife," Ernie said through his fingers, "but nothing happened because I got scared when a car came." He shifted in his seat. "I didn't get any money, either."

Cooley continued to question Ernie about several other open cases from the past six months. These cases had the same MO and similarities in the suspect's description. Ernie adamantly denied being the culprit in these cases, and he denied knowing anything about them. He would admit to nothing more. Without a witness or evidence to link Ernie to any additional cases, Cooley had to focus on the two cases in which Miranda could be criminally charged.

"Ernie, would you complete a written statement about what you did with the girl you put in your car, had sex with, and took her four dollars?"

"Yeah, I can do that."

Cooley gave Ernie a standard form used by the police department for confessions. It contained typed areas and additional lines to be filled in with narrative. The details were listed across the top of the page as follows: Ernest Miranda. Detectives: Carroll Cooley and Wilfred Young. March 13, 1963, 1:30 p.m. The case: Rape D.R. #63–08380. The location was given as Interview Room Two, followed by typed paragraphs:

I, (Miranda's signature), do hereby swear that I make this statement voluntarily and of my own free will, with no threats, coercion, or promises of immunity, and with full knowledge of my legal rights, understanding any statement I make may be used against me.

I, (Miranda's signature), am (23) years of age and have completed the (8th) grade in school.

The statement on the form was written in longhand by Ernie Miranda, and initialed by him at the beginning and end. At the beginning, Ernie wrote his initials, wrote "Picked" in error, crossed it out, and started over with his initials again after "Picked."

eam. ~~Picked~~ eam. Seeing a girl walking up the street stopped a little ahead of her got out of car walked towards her grabbed her by the arm and asked to get in the car. Got in car without force tied hands and ankles. Drove away for a few miles. Stopped asked to take close off. Did not, asked me to take her back home. I started to take close off her without any force and with cooperation. Asked her to lay down and she did. Could not get penis into vagina got about 1/2 (half) inch in. Told her to get close back on. Drove her home. I couldn't say I was sorry for what I had done but asked her to pray for me. eam."

The following was typed on the bottom of the form:

I have read and understand the foregoing

statement and hereby swear to its truthfulness.
(Signed) Ernest A. Miranda
WITNESS: (Signed) Carroll Cooley
(Signed) Wilfred M. Young #182

This was Ernest A. Miranda's written confession to the kidnap, rape, and robbery of Margaret Ann Fair. Although Ernie confessed to other crimes, Detective Cooley did not ask him to write out confessions for those crimes.

After Ernie completed writing his confession, Cooley opened the interview room door and asked Maggie Fair to come over from the detectives' area.

"Margaret, would you come in here, please?"

Detective Young signaled for Maggie to go ahead of him into Interview Room Two. Her eyes widened as she saw the man through the open door. She reluctantly moved forward, taking half steps, and then stopped. She pushed back against the detective herding her into the room. Her legs became week and her vision tunneled down until she could only see the man seated in front of her. Maggie took a deep breath.

"State your name for this young woman," Cooley said.

"Ernie Miranda."

It was the same man that raped her. Maggie was sure of it as soon as she heard his voice. Ernie stared at her through his black horn- rimmed glasses. She dropped her gaze, leaned back into the detective and twisted her shoulders, turning to get away from the man. Detective Young stood fast.

"Do you recognize this woman?" Cooley asked.

"Yes, I recognize her."

Cooley went to Margaret, Young stepped back, and Cooley escorted her out of the room. He shut the door behind him and squared Maggie's shoulders to him. "Margaret, are you okay? Thank you for being so brave."

Maggie said softly, "Detective Cooley, I'm positive that's the man who raped me. I was sure the moment he spoke."

Cooley had Margaret wait with Detective Young and then he escorted Barbara McDaniel to the interview room. He opened the door. Barbara took a deep breath and took a step into the room. She stood firm facing Ernie. Her fingers were interlaced in front of her as she looked at him.

Cooley said, "Please say your name for this lady."

"Ernie Miranda."

"Do you recognize this woman?" Cooley asked.

"Yes, I recognize her," Ernie said. "She talked me out of it. She said she could drive to her apartment and it would be more comfortable. But I said she might have friends there waiting."

Cooley escorted Barbara out of the room. When the door closed behind them Barbara blurted, "That's him, that's the man. I said so many things to him so he wouldn't rape me that night. I forgot I even told him I would drive to my apartment. Now I remember saying that and a lot more. Gosh, I was so scared."

"You did real good in there. You were very brave. Thank you." Cooley said.

Young took Barbara into the detectives' area while Cooley reentered Interview Room Two.

"Ernie, you're under arrest for the kidnap, rape, and robbery of Margaret Fair and the robbery of Barbara McDaniel."

Ernie was handcuffed, led to the elevator, and taken to the City Jail on the fifth floor. An additional charge was added for failure to register with the sheriff's office as an ex-convict.

THE CASE HAD to be written up, all the evidence collected, tested, and the results verified. Sergeant Nealis would review the complete case before it would be submitted to the Maricopa County Attorney's office for prosecution.

Cooley justified having Ernie write out a confession to the Margaret Fair rape and not the McDaniel case because Fair's was the most serious case. In addition, Cooley felt that, by adding more written confessions, the defense attorney would use the unrelated crimes to confuse and create doubt in the minds of jurors. He also believed the attempted rape charge would be harder to prove in the McDaniel case. The Robbery Detective would have to review the McDaniel case and submit it for prosecution on the robbery charge.

The next day, March 14, Cooley went to Good Samaritan

Hospital to obtain Margaret Fair's medical records. This included the lab results of the vaginal smear completed by Dr. J. Haggard as well as a prostatic acid phosphatase test result. The tests, completed on Margaret Fair on March 3, 1963, revealed the presence of sperm without the presence of any sexually transmitted diseases. J. J. Lekos, MD, signed the report.

On March 15, Cooley returned to the City Jail and asked Ernie to sign a Consent to Search form. Once signed and witnessed, this form gave detectives permission to conduct a complete and thorough search of the address and property at the address listed on the form. Miranda signed the form, giving consent to search the home and any vehicles on the property located at 2525 West Mariposa. Detective Cooley and a Maricopa County Sheriff's jailer signed the bottom of the form.

Detectives waited at 2525 West Mariposa Street while Officer Joe Garcia took photographs of the interior and exterior of Ernie's Packard sedan. Detectives subsequently searched the vehicle, finding a small hemp rope located under the front seat. Ernie's home was not searched.

At this point, the Phoenix Police Department had obtained Miranda's written confession, and they had recovered additional evidence against him. The case was reviewed and then submitted for prosecution. All of the procedures used by officers and detectives were consistent with Phoenix Police policy and were conducted in accordance with federal, state, and county laws that were in place at the time.

TEN

ERNESTO MIRANDA'S TRIAL for kidnapping, rape, and robbery proceeded in a manner not uncommon in the early 1960s in Phoenix, Arizona. Cases like Ernie's went through the court system without much notice, let alone notoriety. As far as anyone knew at the time, this case would be like any other.

Ernie could not afford an attorney, so the court appointed a lawyer for him. Alvin Moore, seventy-three years old, was an experienced criminal lawyer with an outstanding record for defending rapists. Mr. Moore reviewed Ernie's history to determine the best defense strategy.

Moore's research revealed that Ernie was six years old when his mother died. Ernie clashed with both his father and his stepmother. Among his siblings, he was close to only one—his brother Ruben. Ernie's brothers had all joined the military as they came of age and Ernie was alone with his father and stepmother.

In 1954 Ernie began getting into trouble. Ernie had nearly completed the eighth grade at Queen of Peace Elementary School in Mesa, Arizona, when he was arrested for burglary. He was convicted and sentenced to probation.

The following year, 1955, Ernie was arrested and convicted of a second burglary. He drew a year in a reform school, serving his time at the Arizona State Industrial School for Boys, located at Fort Grant. Upon Ernie's release in 1956, he was arrested for attempted rape and assault. His conviction got him a two-year sentence in reform school.

At age seventeen, Ernie was released from reform school. He moved to Los Angeles, California, where he was arrested for voyeurism, armed robbery, and curfew violation. He was placed in the county detention home for juveniles. After forty-five days, Ernie turned eighteen. Because he was no longer a juvenile, he had to be released without serving his full sentence.

Ernie returned to Arizona and enlisted in the U.S. Army. He completed boot camp and was assigned to Fort Campbell, Kentucky. Eight months later, he was arrested and placed in the stockade for voyeurism. In addition, Ernie had several counts of AWOL. He was sentenced to six months of hard labor and was ordered to undergo psychiatric counseling. After that, the Army gave him a dishonorable discharge.

Ernie left Kentucky and went to Texas, where he was arrested for vagrancy. When released from jail he went to Nashville, Tennessee. There, Ernie was arrested for driving a stolen vehicle. Because he had driven the stolen car across state lines, he had violated a federal law known as the Dyer Act. Ernie's conviction on that charge got him a year and a day in federal prison. His prison time was divided between two facilities, with six months in Chillicothe, Ohio, and the remaining six months and a day in Lompoc, California.

When Ernest Miranda came out of prison in California in 1961, he met Twila Hoffman. She was twenty-nine years old, white, and the mother of a son and daughter, both under ten years of age. Twila was separated from her husband.

They moved to Mesa, Arizona. Twila and Ernie had a baby girl in the late summer of 1962. Ernie worked nights on the loading dock of a produce company in Phoenix. Twila worked at a nursery school.

Upon reviewing Ernie's history, the police reports, and all of the evidence in the cases against him, Alvin Moore filed a notice with the court. The notice stated that Ernie's defense would be a plea of insanity. An insanity plea meant that psychiatrists from both the defense and the state would have to examine Ernie and determine if he was sane enough to stand trial for the charges against him.

A summary of the psychiatrists' examinations stated, in part, that Ernie had "a full elementary education and that, although he had an emotional illness, he had sufficient mentality and emotional stability to understand what he was doing when he was doing it, and to fully appreciate all the potential consequences of his act." Having received this information, Mr. Moore abandoned the insanity defense.

THE TWO CASES involving Margaret Fair and Barbara McDaniel were set for trial. Alvin Moore served as the defense attorney in both cases. Judge Yale McFate presided over both trials.

The first trial was held June 18, 1963, in the Superior Court of Maricopa County, Arizona. The charge: robbery. The victim: Barbara McDaniel.

The crime occurred on November 27, 1962. In this case, Ernie allegedly forced his way into Barbara's Ford Galaxie and drove Barbara to the alley behind the Phoenix Credit Bureau. There he attempted to rape her at knifepoint. Barbara talked Ernie out of raping her. He then robbed her—also at knifepoint.

Barbara McDaniel had identified Ernie at Phoenix Police headquarters on March 13, 1963, as the man who had kidnapped her, attempted to rape her, and then robbed her of eight dollars. During the trial, Barbara confirmed the identity of her attacker. The court found Ernie guilty of the robbery charge.

The Maricopa County Superior Court held a second trial the following week. This time the victim was Margaret Fair and the charges were kidnapping, rape, and robbery. Deputy County Attorney Laurence Turoff served as prosecutor. Margaret Fair, Susanne Williamson, and detectives Cooley and Young gave testimony for the prosecution.

The second trial proceeded routinely until Alvin Moore began cross-examining Detective Cooley. Moore asked Cooley how he had obtained Ernie Miranda's written confession.

"Officer Cooley, in the taking of this statement, what did you say to the defendant to get him to make this statement?"

"I asked the defendant if he would write the same story that he just told me, and he said that he would," Cooley answered.

"Did you warn him of his rights?"

"Yes, sir, at the heading of the statement is a paragraph typed out, and I read this paragraph to him out loud."

"I don't see in the statement that it says where he is entitled to the advice of an attorney before he made it," Moore said.

"No, sir," Cooley replied.

"Is it not your practice to advise people you arrest that they are entitled to the services of an attorney before they make a statement?"

"No, sir."

Moore objected to the confession being submitted as evidence. Judge Yale McFate allowed the written confession into evidence, because it was consistent with the law and common police procedures at the time.

IT WAS ACCEPTED practice for Phoenix Police officers and detectives to obtain a confession from a suspect and then ask them if the statement was true. If the suspect said the statement was true, un-coerced, and without promise of favor, the officer or detective would ask the suspect to write out this information in their confession. The form used in Phoenix had been revised in 1959 and had been accepted readily by the courts into the 1960s.

In addition, the constitutional right to silence and to have an attorney present did not extend to questioning by police officers. The right to remain silent and the right to an attorney meant that you were not compelled to testify against yourself in a court of law and that you had the right to have an attorney with you in that court.

Moore emphasized the weaknesses of the prosecution's case in his closing argument.

"Miss Fair claimed to have been a virgin prior to the attack. However, the doctors who completed the hospital examination said she was not. Miss Fair could not remember the exact chronology of the night's events. Miss Fair was bound with rope. However, she did not exhibit any bruising or abrasions after the attack.

"You have in this case a sorrowful case, but you don't have the facts to require that you send a man to prison for rape of a woman who should have resisted and resisted and resisted, until her resistance was at least overcome by the force and violence of the defendant."

To resist was an essential requirement under Arizona law at that time. Anything less was regarded as the victim's compliance. It would take until 1977 for the Arizona legislature to enact a thorough criminal code revision, the first since 1913. The new code would modernize the outdated territorial laws and included the revision of sexual assault and related offenses.

Deputy County Attorney Turoff completed his closing argument with the following comment: "The victim did not enter into this act of intercourse with him [Miranda] willfully, but in fact she was forced to, by his own force and violence, directed against her."

The jury returned a guilty verdict for the kidnapping, rape, and robbery of Margaret Fair.

JUNE 27, 1963, Judge McFate sentenced Miranda on both the Barbara Sue McDaniel case and the Margaret Fair case. Miranda drew two concurrent terms of twenty to thirty years in prison. Attorney Alvin Moore promptly stated that he would file an appeal on the grounds that Detective Cooley had obtained Miranda's written confession in the Margaret Fair rape case illegally, by denying him his constitutional right to legal counsel.

Nevertheless, the cases against Miranda had been adjudicated through the court, and there was little reason for the victims, the witnesses, or the detectives to think that Ernie Miranda would someday reappear in their society.

IN LIGHT OF the Ernest Miranda case, the County Attorney's office requested that the Phoenix Police Department be more cautious during their interrogations. They suggested reading suspects the federal form used for confessions, prior to interrogations—the same form Detective Cooley used to advise Ernie Miranda of his rights *after* Ernie's verbal confession. As a result of the County Attorney's policy, new methods would come into play when Detective Sergeant Nealis led his team through the process of convicting a serial armed robber named Frank Stacy.

ELEVEN

CECIL STAMPER DROVE his 1955 Mercury two-door into the alley behind the Sands Motel on Van Buren Street. Stamper had one passenger—his friend, Frankie Stacy. It was 1:45 a.m. on Thursday morning, August 22, 1963.

"Whatta we doin' here?" Cecil asked.

"It finally stopped raining. I'm gonna get us some money," Frankie said.

"Hey, take the empty beer bottles with ya, huh? Keep my car nice."

"Yeah, okay, I'll do that," Frankie said sarcastically.

Frankie opened the passenger door, got out of the car, and looked around. He untucked his shirt so that it fell below his waistline. He reached under the front seat and retrieved a Smith & Wesson .38 Special revolver with a six-inch barrel. He stuffed it in his front waistband. Then he removed a .357 Magnum Colt Python handgun from the glove box.

"Whoa, you ain't gonna need no arsenal, Frankie." Cecil's eighteen-year-old voice came out strained. "You said it was just one old guy, right?"

"Hey, I ain't gonna need the Python, but just in case…" Frankie put the second handgun in his waistband at the small of his back. *If I look at Cecil again I might lose my confidence.* Frankie looked away, closed the car door, and disappeared into the darkness of the alley.

Frankie Stacy, at nineteen, had committed armed robberies in California and thought it would be even easier in "laid back" Arizona. His dark green shirt and Levi's would make him less visible at night. His black curly hair stood out on all sides of his head. He planned to get a haircut the next morning to make himself less recognizable.

Frankie walked cautiously across the wet parking lot, dotted with puddles, and entered the back door of the motel. The door scraped the floor as it opened inward toward the lobby. There were no customers at this hour, and the only employee working was George Scheerer, Jr., the forty-one-year-old desk clerk.

George looked up from mopping the rainwater that had leaked into the office behind the counter. He watched the small young man walk around to the front of the registration desk.

"May I help you?" George asked.

Frankie drew the Smith & Wesson from his front waistband, pointed it at the clerk, and said, "Give me the money and don't push any buzzer."

"Okay, okay, just take it easy." George raised his hands in a surrender position, and his mop handle fell against the wall behind the counter. He tried not to shake when he opened the cash drawer. He had to remove the drawer and place it on the counter so the gunman could reach it. Frankie's curly hair, his face, and an arched arm with a gun in its hand were all George could see over the high countertop. Looking down the barrel of the handgun, George realized it was similar to looking into a large, empty trash can.

"Give me the bills," Frankie demanded.

George gathered bills of various denominations from the drawer and slowly handed them to the robber. Frankie grabbed the money and shoved it into his front pants pocket. He then reached into the drawer and took the half-dollars. He reached in again and took the quarters. "Give me the money from under the drawer," Frankie waved the gun, then pointed it to where the drawer had been removed.

"That's all there is," George said. "You can come back here and look for yourself."

"Hell, it ain't hardly worth it," Frankie yelled. *Aw, damn, and I touched the drawer.*

"Take that cloth on the counter there and wipe off the cash drawer, old man."

George took the cleaning rag and wiped the empty cash drawer.

"Now, move back and get in that closet," Frankie pointed the gun toward the closet door. George moved to the west wall and opened the broom closet door. He stepped inside and closed the door behind him. George closed his eyes, stood very still, and listened. He remained in this position until he heard the motel's rear door scrape the floor when Frankie left. George sighed with relief, put a hand on the doorknob and took a breath. He went to the switchboard and called the Phoenix police.

The call came in at 1:52 a.m. Officer James Adams would arrive a few minutes later to take the armed robbery report.

ONCE OUTSIDE, FRANKIE looked around, saw no one, and ran quickly across the wet parking lot to the alley, where he got into the waiting car. Cecil drove his Mercury down the alley unnoticed.

The two men cruised around town for a while. The rain had brought down the ninety-degree daytime temperature to a much cooler seventy-five degrees. They rolled with the car windows down. Before long, they returned to the west side of Phoenix and continued westbound on Camelback Road.

"We're outta beer, Frankie, and I wanna get rid of the beer bottles. They're stinkin' up my car."

Frankie was quiet, thinking.

"So what happened in the motel?"

"Pull in at the 7-Eleven, then," Frankie said. "They have a trash can."

CECIL PULLED IN at a 7-Eleven convenience store on the southwest corner of 67th Avenue and Camelback Road, parking in a space where the store lights illuminated the car interior.

"Here's your cut, that's what happened in the motel," Frankie said, handing Cecil some dollar bills. Cecil shoved the bills in his shirt pocket.

Cecil then collected the empty beer bottles and threw them in the 7-Eleven's trash can. When he returned to the car he slid his car seat forward, reached in, and pulled up the backseat. He took the money out of his pocket, laid out thirty-two one-dollar bills, and put the seat back on top of the money. He adjusted the front seat and slid back in behind the steering wheel, looking over at Frankie. "What are you doin' with your hands in your pants, Frankie?"

"I'm puttin' my share of the money inside my shorts. I can't get caught with this much money on me...I'm supposed to be broke, you know."

Cecil started the car. Frankie settled into his seat and looked at his watch. "Just take me to my sister's place, it's already three o'clock."

Cecil drove south on 67th Avenue and turned right onto Wolf Street, made another quick right turn on 67th Drive, and parked the Mercury in the street in front of 6718 West Pierson. Cecil remembered the house because it was right where 67th Drive curved into Pierson Street. Cecil turned off the lights and the engine.

Headlights suddenly shone into the car from in front of them, blinding Cecil and Frankie. The vehicle blocked in the Mercury from the front. Detectives Ralph Cluff and Richard "Dick" Murphey yelled, "Phoenix Police—get your hands up." Flashlights blazed in Cecil and Frankie's eyes.

Detective Cluff said, "Frank Stacy, you're under arrest for an armed robbery warrant outta California."

Murphey jerked Cecil out the driver-side door while Cluff swung the passenger door open, pulled Frankie out, and slammed him against the side of the car. Cluff's shoulder struck Frankie between the shoulder blades, taking away his breath and his desire to fight or run. Cluff kicked Frankie's feet wide apart. Frankie instinctively threw his hands on the car's roof, trying to balance himself.

Cluff reached under Frankie's un-tucked shirttail and ran his hand over Frankie's waistband.

"Gun, partner," Cluff yelled to Murphey. Cluff stuck the Smith & Wesson handgun in his own waistband and kept searching.

"Second gun, Murphey, watch your guy. He probably has one too."

Cluff peeled the Colt Python out of Frankie's waistband and kept searching, finding a roll of coins in Frankie's shirt pocket. Cluff held the roll of coins in his flashlight beam, noticing a blue wrapper. He shoved the roll into Frankie's front pants pocket, then handcuffed Frankie behind his back.

Detective Murphey kept Cecil pinned against the driver's side of the car. Murphey had already asked once. He asked a second time, "Where's the gun?"

"I told you, I don't have a gun on me," Cecil said, trying to breathe. Murphey smelled beer on Cecil's breath when he spoke.

"You're under nineteen. I'm placing you under arrest for 'minor consuming alcohol'." Murphey then pulled Cecil's hands behind his back and handcuffed him. Murphey jerked Cecil away from the car and looked inside the open driver-side window for any evidence to support his charge in addition to Cecil's breath. He didn't see any beer bottles. He took a wallet out of Cecil's back pocket and lit it up with a flashlight. The Arizona driver's license in the wallet identified his captive as Cecil Clair Stamper, age eighteen.

"What are you doin' with Frank Stacy?" Murphey asked. "And I don't want any lip."

"We were just driving around."

"When did you start 'just driving around'?" Murphey asked.

"Ten o'clock, ten thirty."

"Whatta you guys been doin' since ten or ten thirty?"

"We had a few beers and drove around with a couple girls. Then we dropped them off."

"Then what?"

"We just drove around till now."

"How long have you known Frank Stacy, Cecil?"

"Uh, going on about six years, I guess."

"Six years, huh? You guys must've gone to school together."

"Yeah."

"Then what happens? Frank goes to California, he comes back, and you guys pal around."

Cecil stayed quiet.

"You know what I think, Cecil...I think you guys have been out committin' crimes tonight."

Cecil didn't answer.

"You know your buddy Frank there has a warrant outta California on a robbery beef?"

Cecil shrugged his shoulders. "We ain't done anything that would be of interest to the police department."

The detectives stuffed the handcuffed suspects into two different patrol cars that had arrived as back up.

THE PATROL OFFICERS delivered Cecil and Frankie to police headquarters and marched them over to the detective bureau. It was 3:30 a.m. when officers placed Cecil in Interview Room Four and Frankie in Interview Room Five. Murphey had driven Cecil's Mercury to the station and parked it on Jefferson Street.

The detectives lit cigarettes and conferred. "We've got Frank Stacy on the armed robbery warrant," Cluff said. "We'll talk to him first. All I need is a signature on a waiver of extradition for the robbery and then we'll find out what they've been up to tonight."

"These guys are active," Murphey said. "I'd sure like to know what robberies they've been doin' here."

"Excuse me, detectives," said the officer who had transported Frank Stacy to the station. "I asked Stacy to empty his pockets on the table in the interview room, which he did. He had a billfold with thirty one-dollar bills and two driver's licenses in his name. One from California and the other one's from Illinois. He also had some change, five half-dollars, thirty-seven quarters, and five dollars in dimes. The dimes were rolled in a blue wrapper."

Officer James Adams then entered the bureau and said, "Hey, Detective Cluff, I just took an armed robbery report at the Sands Motel, thirty-three hundred block of East Van Buren. It was just before two o'clock. Can I look at your guys and see if they match the description of my robber?"

"What's the description?" Cluff asked.

"I'll read what I've got from the clerk. White male, eighteen to twenty-one years, five foot two to five foot three, one-twenty to one twenty-five, small build and a sallow complexion, curly and unruly black hair, wearing a dark green short-sleeved sport shirt."

Frank Stacy fit the description of the suspect in the Sands Motel robbery. The detectives read Officer Adams's report and took a cigarette break. Murphey and Cluff then entered Interview Room Five. Metal chairs scraped the floor as they pulled them out, slid into them, and sat across the table from Frankie.

"Where'd you go tonight, Frank?" Cluff asked.

Frankie sniffed and shifted in his chair, "I was at my sister's house, that's where I'm stayin'. That's where I stay when I'm in town."

"How much money did you leave your sister's house with?" Cluff asked.

"Three dollars and some change."

"How do you account for the additional change and dollar bills in your wallet, huh, Frank?"

Frankie didn't answer. He bit his lower lip, dragging his upper teeth across it until his lip slipped away from his teeth.

"I'll tell what I think, Frank," Cluff said. "I think you held up the Sands Motel."

During the course of the interview, Frank didn't deny the robbery, yet he refused to admit he committed it. The detectives thought he would talk, but only if they changed their approach.

"Some of the money taken in the motel robbery is still missing, Frank," Cluff said. "If we can recover all of the money it'll look better for you. Where do you think the money is? Does Cecil have it?"

Frankie lowered his head and fixed his eyes on the table. "No, I've got it. It's in my shorts." Frankie then reached into the back of his Levi's and into his underwear. He removed five tens and four fives and placed them on the table.

"Why'd you do it, Frank?" Cluff asked.

"Maybe the robber has a wife in California and he needed the money to go and return her to Phoenix to live with him."

"Do you have a wife in California, Frank?" Cluff asked in a softer tone.

"Yeah."

"Were you trying to get money to go to her and bring her back with you to Arizona?"

"Yeah."

Cluff counted the money and asked, "So tell me, Frank, how do you account for the one-hundred nineteen dollars and seventy-five cents I found in your pockets and in your shorts?"

Frankie didn't answer. Instead, he looked down at the table and shook his head side to side.

"You know this'll all be taken care of when you're identified in a lineup by the clerk from the Sands Motel."

Frankie kept looking at the table, his brows furrowed and his lips tightened. He nodded his head up and down.

"You took three handguns in that robbery in California," Cluff said. "I took two of 'em off you. I'll get those guns returned to their rightful owners…But we need to return the third gun to its rightful owner, also." He paused. "Where's the third gun, Frank?"

"It's in the Mercury…in the glove box."

Frankie got a ride on the elevator to the City Jail on the fifth floor. At 5:20 a.m., he was booked on one count of armed robbery of the Sands Motel and one count of carrying concealed weapons. In addition, the Phoenix detectives put a hold on Frankie on behalf of the San Jose Police Department for the armed robbery warrant in that jurisdiction.

DETECTIVES CLUFF AND Murphey stepped into Interview Room Four and seated themselves across the metal table from Cecil Stamper. Cecil sat with his elbows on the table, nibbling on a thumbnail.

"Cecil," Cluff began, "you're in a lot of trouble here." He paused for effect. "The only way we can help you is if you help us."

Cecil took his hand away from his mouth. "How do I do that?"

"I have reason to believe there's stolen property in your car. I'd like your permission to remove that stolen property."

Cecil spread his hands out, palms up. "Sure, if there's stolen property in my car, I want it out."

Cluff and Murphey nodded to each other. Murphey got up, obtained a flashlight, and went outside to Cecil's Mercury. Murphey searched the passenger areas of the car. He lifted the lower portion of the backseat on the driver's side. Under the seat, he found thirty-two one-dollar bills neatly laid out.

Murphey had Cecil's car keys, but the glove box was unlocked. Murphey opened it and removed a Smith & Wesson .357 Magnum. He held the gun in his left hand and released the revolver's cylinder. The cylinder swung out, exposing the unfired cartridges. Murphey located the serial number on the frame of the gun in the yoke area— K412072. The number matched the third of the three handguns taken during the sporting goods store robbery in San Jose, California.

Murphey secured the evidence he had recovered from the Mercury and returned to Interview Room Four. He closed the door behind him and stood over Cecil Stamper.

Cluff leaned back in his chair, silently giving Murphey the lead. They had been partners long enough to play off each other and Cecil wasn't talking to Cluff.

"Thirty-two one-dollar bills…How did this money get in your car, Cecil?"

Cecil stared up at the detective without blinking. "I have no idea."

Murphey placed his palms down on the table in front of Cecil, bent his elbows slightly, and leaned in. He put his nose inches from Cecil's nose, and looked into Cecil's eyes. "C'mon, Cecil, we're talking about armed robbery here. The Sands Motel on Van Buren gets knocked over, the night clerk describes your buddy Frank as the gunman. That leaves you as the driver of the getaway car. Half of the money is in your backseat and a stolen gun outta California is in your glove box." Murphey pushed off the table and stood tall, his hands at his side. "With that alone, all by itself, I know a jury will convict you. You might as well tell us about it."

"All right, all right, I'll tell ya," Cecil said, thinking fast.

A metal chair raked the floor as Murphey pulled it out from the table and sat down. Cluff shoved a notepad in front of Murphey and laid a pencil on it.

Cecil's voice became louder. "I had no idea Frankie was gonna rob anyone." He leaned in toward Murphey. Murphey wrote. Cecil had his arms crossed, elbows on the table. He waited for Murphey to look up before he continued. "I drove the car to the alley. Frankie got out, said he had to piss. He wasn't gone long enough to pull a robbery. He came back, got in the car, and I drove down the alley to 32nd Place out to Van Buren."

"Then what'd you do?" Murphey asked.

Cecil leaned back, put his hands on the table, palms up and open. His voice softened. "I drove across town toward Frankie's sister's house."

"Then what?"

"At uh, 67th Avenue and Camelback Frankie said to pull into the 7-Eleven."

"You're doin' good. Then what?"

"Frankie told me he held up the Sands Motel and gave me a wad of bills."

"What'd ya tell Frank then? Did you try to refuse the money? You knew it was stolen at that point."

"No, I didn't refuse it," Cecil's head dropped, eyes on the tabletop. "I took the money and put it in my shirt pocket."

Murphey put his arms on the table, closed his fists, and leaned in, looking at Cecil. "You're lyin'."

"I'm not lyin'."

"There's two ways to lie, Cecil. One is to say something that's not true. The other is to lie by omission..." Murphey's voice softened. "You know, by leaving things out. I don't think you're a liar, Cecil. I just think you left out a few things."

"Okay," Cecil said. "You're right. I'm not a liar, I just left some stuff out."

"Let's start from the beginning. What'd you two do before you went to the motel?"

Cecil told the whole story, beginning with earlier in the evening, into the night, and up until when the detectives pulled him and Frankie out of his car.

"Okay, Cecil," Murphey said. "I need one more thing from you."

"What's that? I told you everything."

"I would like you to write out your side of the story on paper...Will you do that?"

"Sure, I can do that," Cecil said.

Once Cecil Stamper completed his written confession, the detectives read it over. Then Murphey said, "All right, Cecil, you came clean. Now, you understand, you're still goin' to be booked into jail for armed robbery and minor consuming alcohol."

"Yeah...What's gonna happen to my car? It's my baby."

"Cars are a lot easier to impound than they are to get released to their owner. After towing fees and storage fees it gets expensive. Do you understand what I'm saying?" Murphey asked.

"Yes, sir, easy to impound a car, harder to get it out, and it costs money."

"Because you came clean here and you wrote it all down, I'm gonna let you have someone you trust come and get your fifty-five Mercury instead of impounding it."

"You'll do that?" Cecil asked.

"Just give me a name and number."

"Uh, Jack Weme. His phone number is BR5-3116. He lives at 4714 East McKinley."

DAY SHIFT DETECTIVE Sergeant Nealis completed a triage of his in-box and drank a cup of black coffee. He reviewed the Sands Motel armed robbery report. Cluff and Murphey's case looked fairly sound, but for whatever reason, Cluff and Murphey had not followed a recent directive that had come down from the chief. The two detectives had caught the robbers and interrogated them in the way they always had—a way that was accepted practice by the department and the courts. Nealis believed that the County Attorney would not file charges against Stacy and Stamper unless something more was done.

Nealis called day-shift Detectives Scott Chestnut and Donald Procunier into his office. "I'd like to tie this case up tight," Nealis told them. "Conduct a live lineup with the victim. Then read the suspects their rights and re-interview them."

Detectives Chestnut and Procunier conducted a live lineup in Interview Room Four at 8:30 a.m. The lineup consisted of three prisoners along with suspect Franklin Stacy, who was third in the line.

George W. Sheerer, Jr., the victim of the Sands Motel armed

robbery, arrived at police headquarters. Detective Procunier greeted him and explained the live lineup.

"Do you have a problem with identifying the man who robbed you?" Procunier asked.

"No, sir. I believe I could recognize him."

Procunier and Chestnut then led Mr. Sheerer into Interview Room 4 to view the men in the lineup. Each man had an 8½x11-inch white card hanging around his neck. Mr. Sheerer froze in the doorway.

"Are you all right?" Procunier asked.

Mr. Sheerer whispered in Procunier's ear. "I thought you meant to look at him in a jail cell or from some distance, not in the same room."

"Let me assure you that you're safe, and after the trial you'll never see him again."

A table separated the men in the live lineup from the detectives, who stood on either side of Mr. Sheerer.

"Have you ever seen anybody on the other side of this room prior to this time?" asked Procunier

Mr. Scheerer answered, "Yes, I have."

"Which of the subjects have you seen prior to this time?"

"Number Three."

"Where have you seen subject Number Three before? Can you give me a day?"

"At the Sands Motel on August twenty-second, nineteen sixty-three."

"Under what condition did you see this subject?"

Mr. Sheerer pointed at Frankie. "This is the man that robbed me at the Sands Motel."

Detective Chestnut finished writing down Mr. Sheerer's responses to Procunier's questions, put down his notepad, and placed his left hand on Franklin Stacy's shoulder. "Is this the person that you're referring to, Mr. Sheerer?"

"Yes, it is," Scheerer said.

Chestnut gathered his notepad, and the detectives ushered Sheerer out of the room. At 8:45 a.m. Records and Information Bureau Officer William MacGill took a picture of the lineup.

Chestnut then re-interviewed Franklin Joe Stacy and read the federal form out loud to him at 8:55 a.m. Stacy began his story from when he arrived in Phoenix from San Jose on August 16, 1963, on American Airlines Flight 86. The plane arrived at 6:10 p.m. Frank said his friend Cecil C. Stamper met him at the airport. Cecil drove to Frank's sister's residence at 6718 West Pierson. Frankie then told the same story that he told Cluff and Murphey. The interrogation concluded at 9:30 a.m.

Officers brought Cecil C. Stamper from the City Jail to the robbery detectives' area at 9:40 a.m. He was advised of his right to an attorney and told that anything that he wrote down, or said, could be used in court against him. Cecil was asked to review the statement he had previously given to detectives Murphey and Cluff and to specifically read the information at the top of the federal form. He read the form and reviewed the statement he had written. Then he told the detectives, "I came clean."

The detectives had Cecil retell his story. After reading his rights Cecil told his story but denied any prior knowledge that Frank Stacy intended to rob the Sands Motel. The interrogation ended at 11:10 a.m. An officer led Cecil to the elevator and returned him to the City Jail.

The Sands Motel robbery marks the starting point at which the Phoenix Police Department began reading suspects their rights. Franklin Stacy was booked for armed robbery, carrying concealed weapons, and for an armed robbery warrant issued in California. He would not be back on the streets for some time to come. Cecil Stamper recanted his statement about knowing Frankie Stacy intended to rob the Sands Motel. Phoenix PD charged him only with possession of stolen property and minor consumption of alcohol.

Neither Stacy nor Stamper experienced due process procedures in quite the same way as Ernest Miranda. It would be years before the Phoenix Police Department's new policy became the legal standard for the entire nation.

TWELVE

ERNIE MIRANDA, SITTING in prison in Florence, Arizona, had no idea his arrest had triggered policy changes in the Phoenix Police Department. Carroll Cooley, Miranda's arresting officer, continued to work the Crimes Against Persons Detail in the Phoenix Police Detective Bureau. Miranda had been in prison less than two months when Cooley experienced a life-changing event, which arrived in the form of young man named Christopher Flener.

AT 9:00 P.M., on Friday, August 23, 1963, nineteen-year-old Christopher Flener stood in the open front door of his mother's house at 13th Street and Glenrosa, snapping the buttons on his light blue cowboy shirt.

"Where are you going?" his mother called from the living room.

"Just out, I said, all right?" He slammed the door. *Jeez, why does she want to know everything I do?*

Flener picked up the newspaper in the front yard on the way out to his car. He climbed behind the wheel of the first car he actually owned. He pumped the gas pedal several times, depressed the clutch, and turned the ignition key. The engine started with a rumble. He turned on the dome light, picked up the newspaper, and opened it to the page with the news article on the Center City Motel robbery. He smiled big and tossed the paper onto the gray cloth passenger seat.

Flener thought he made a great deal when he bought this 1953 two-door Ford Mainline. Between the motel robberies and his paycheck from his job at the Ramada Inn, he was able not only to have purchased the vehicle but to still have seventy-three dollars in his wallet.

He slid his hands up and down the big steering wheel from the twelve o'clock position to the bottom of the wheel at six o'clock and then back to twelve. He turned on the radio to his favorite station, put the shifter in reverse, and backed into the street. He put the car in first gear, spun the steering wheel, and headed the car down 13th street.

By 9:30 p.m., he was cruising Van Buren Street, looking for motels to rob. Flener had robbed both the Stone and the Center City Motels. He obtained the most money from the Center City Motel at 600 West Van Buren Street on Monday night. It was time for another visit.

DETECTIVES CARROLL COOLEY and Dave Haynes were working second shift. All of the detectives rotated into the second shift assignment for two weeks and it was their turn. The detectives picked up desk sergeant Al Edens from police headquarters to take him out for coffee. Edens appreciated the gesture because he was not assigned a car and generally didn't leave the station during his shift.

When the trio walked into Helsing's Restaurant at 601 West Van Buren Street, Sergeant Edens was still giving Haynes a hard time. "Haynes, where'd you learn how to drive? Next time Cooley drives." Edens stopped abruptly and looked around the crowded restaurant. "For cryin' out loud, the whole second shift is in here."

"It's the best place for a cuppa coffee after nine p.m., Sarge," Cooley said.

"Lighten up, boss," Haynes said. "Most of 'em have rank, anyway. There's only one marked unit in the lot and only two patrol officers in here. That doesn't even violate the two marked cars policy."

The sergeant shook his head. The three men slid into an empty booth against the front window near the main entrance.

"What the heck you carrying, Haynes? That hog leg jabbed me in the hip gettin' into the seat."

"It's a .357 just like Cooley's. I don't hear you givin' him grief."

"There's a difference," Cooley said. "Dave loads his own ammo. They're a lot hotter load than what I carry. I carry standard rounds. Dave's bullets would go through a tree trunk."

"What are you sayin', Carroll—I'm not in policy?"

"I didn't say that," Cooley said.

"You better be in policy, Haynes," the sergeant said.

"I'm in policy, boss. Cooley's just jealous because I've got hotter loads than he does."

"These are good seats," Cooley said, "right across the street from the Center City Motel."

"Yeah, it was robbed Monday night," Haynes said.

The waitress brought the detectives three cups of coffee. "Anything else I can get you, fellas?"

The sergeant looked up and answered politely, "No, but thank you, this'll do it for now." He then turned his attention to Cooley. "Down to business, why are you fellows hell-bent on the Center City Motel? There's too many cops in this area this time of night, and it makes no sense that anyone would risk getting caught."

"If they weren't stupid we wouldn't catch 'em, boss," Haynes said. "Besides, Center City was hit around nine-fifty p.m. The Sands Hotel at 3300 East Van Buren got hit at two a.m. on Thursday. But Cluff and Murphey arrested two guys for that robbery. We think the same guy that hit Center City also robbed the Stone Motel at 2100 East Van Buren last night after 8:30 p.m."

"Same MO?" the sergeant asked.

"What's similar is the guy who hit the Stone and Center City wore a handkerchief over the lower part of his face. He used a pair of black-framed sunglasses, probably to keep the handkerchief from falling off of his face."

"But Center City was taken for two hundred and eighty bucks," Haynes said. "The other motels got took for half that."

"So you fellows figure they might hit Center City again," Edens said. "Where there any vehicles, suspicious or otherwise, seen in the area?"

"The clerks were put on the floor face down. They told us the suspect left on foot. No one we've interviewed heard or saw a vehicle once the suspect left," Cooley said.

WHILE THE DETECTIVES drank coffee, a 1953 Ford Mainline drove from Van Buren north into the alley between 5th and 6th avenues. There was nothing unusual about the Washington blue Ford or the male driver.

This will be easy as last time, Chris Flener thought as he continued north for about half of the city block. He parked behind a closed business at 365 North 6th Avenue. Flener took a handkerchief and a pair of black sunglasses from the glove box. He left his wallet on the seat of the car so he could fill all of his pockets with cash and jewelry. Flener then pulled a J. C. Higgins 9-shot .22 caliber revolver from the glove box. The blue steel, cowboy-styled gun had a 5½-inch barrel. He opened the action and checked the cartridges. He spun the cylinder and snapped the action closed. He twirled the gun like the TV show cowboys did. He was ready. He had his cowboy shirt on, his mask, and his pistol. All the confidence he would need, same as twice before.

Flener walked south down the alley, then crossed a lot heading west to the City Center Motel. He entered the office, pointed his gun at the clerk, and said, "Sit down—drop!"

"Okay, just don't shoot me," Mel Husband said as he sat on the floor behind the counter.

Flener grew excited thinking of the easy money. He moved quickly to the cash drawer, pulled it open, took all of the bills, and put them in his back pockets. He snatched up the coins and put them in his front pockets. Flener then removed the cash box from the cash drawer and pulled it under his arm. He pointed his gun at Mel and said, "Crawl over and give me the jewelry." Mel crawled to the end of the counter, grabbed jewelry from the shelf and gave it to the robber. "Where's the safe?"

"It's in the back but only the manager can open it," Mel said. "And he's not here now."

TWO of the uniformed officers in Helsing's Restaurant were Lieutenant George Sanders and a reserve police officer named Sam Leabo. Cooley noticed they abruptly slid out of their booth, hurried past the detectives, and went out the front entrance. The waitress for those officers still stood at their table and remained there like a statue, pointing at the Center City Motel. Then the rest of the police officers in Helsing's reacted at once. They looked across Van Buren and into the lighted lobby of the Center City Motel, seeing a man with a handkerchief on his face and a gun in his hand. The motel clerk crouched behind the counter.

Lieutenant Sanders found two plainclothes sergeants in the parking lot, Blaine Thompson and Sam Howe. The two sergeants had just left the restaurant and were in their vehicle when they saw the commotion. They quickly devised a plan to have Lieutenant Sanders and the reserve officer take a position to the rear of the motel on the north side. The sergeants would cover the entrance that faced south.

Sergeant Howe used his radio to notify the dispatcher. "Fifty-one John, we have an armed robbery in progress at six hundred West Van Buren. Suspect is a white male, five-foot seven inches, one hundred thirty to one hundred forty pounds, wearing a blue shirt and dark trousers. He's got a handkerchief covering his face and black sunglasses. He's holding a handgun on the clerk. Request units to arrive from the north side of the motel. We have the south side covered."

"Ten–four, fifty-one John," responded the dispatcher. He then repeated the information to all patrol units.

The two sergeants began to set up a perimeter of officers to seal off the suspect's escape routes. They directed the first officer to arrive on the scene to 7th Avenue at Grand and Van Buren, the closest intersection to stop traffic. The next patrol vehicle was assigned to 5th Avenue and Van Buren Street.

Before additional officers could arrive, Detectives Cooley and Haynes, followed by Sergeant Edens, ran out of Helsing's front door. They bolted past the sergeants holding the south perimeter, moving at a dead run toward the Center City Motel.

"GET DOWN ON the floor behind the counter," Flener said to the clerk. He then ran out of the motel office door, across the parking lot, and northeast across 6th Avenue. He suddenly realized that men in dress shirts and ties were chasing him. Flener ran past 6th Avenue and through a vacant lot. He threw the cash box down and fled north into the darkened alley between 5th and 6th avenues.

Detective Haynes ran with his .357 handgun out and shouted, "Stop or we'll shoot!" Running ahead of Haynes and twenty feet behind the suspect, with his .357 in his hand, Cooley was closing in. Flener ran with his gun in his right hand. He reached across his chest and put the gun under his left armpit, pointing at the officer behind him. He pulled the trigger. A loud *pop* immediately resounded. The officer stopped chasing him. Flener kept running, jumped a three-foot fence out of the alley, climbed over a pile of wood as high as the fence, and hid in the darkness. He crouched under the outside staircase of an apartment building, heart pounding, ears ringing from the report of the handgun.

Something had exploded in Carroll Cooley's head. He stopped running and grabbed his face with his left hand. He spit out blood and a tooth. *I think I've been shot.*

Haynes ran ahead into the darkness of the alley. It was too dark to see, and he had no idea where the suspect was, so he ran back to where Cooley stood with Sergeant Edens. All three men were out of breath.

Bleeding profusely from his mouth Cooley mumbled, "I think I've been shot." More blood gushed out as he leaned forward.

Edens grabbed Cooley around the shoulders and steadied him. "I'll need your gun, Carroll. It's policy."

Patrolman Simmons drove up the alley to the detectives' location. "A police ambulance is en route, Sarge," Simmons said.

Cooley gave his gun to Sergeant Edens, knowing that if you were in a shooting, policy dictated that you turn over your weapon. Cooley climbed into the back seat of the patrol car.

Edens got into the front seat and said, "Simmons, get us to Memorial Hospital. Now!"

The call went out over the police radio: "An officer had been shot." Every available patrol unit and the newspaper men who monitored the police converged on the alley between 5th and 6th avenues north of Van Buren Street.

Detective Haynes ran to the detective car he had parked at Helsing's restaurant. He jumped in and quickly drove back to the alley. In the few minutes after the shooting, the cavalry had arrived. Officers left their vehicles at the mouth of the alley and ran down the alley, looking for the suspect. Police car headlights illuminated the cloud of dust that hadn't yet settled in their wake. Haynes heard the officers yelling as they ran down the alley and fanned out into the neighborhood with flashlights lit and guns drawn, determined to avenge Detective Carroll Cooley.

The shouting dissipated as Haynes crossed his wrists, holding his flashlight in his left hand and his .357 in his right. The beam of light shone where the revolver pointed as he walked down the alley. His search started at the puddle of blood where Cooley was hit. Haynes was alone now as he looked for clues in the pitch darkness. He stalked down the alley, methodically sweeping the flashlight back and forth to each fence line and covering the area between.

Forty feet into the alley from where Cooley was shot, Haynes shone his flashlight on a white picket fence to his right. On the other side of the fence sat a three-foot-high pile of wood. Just past the wood stack, and under an outside staircase to the rear of an apartment building, Haynes saw a figure. The man crouched under the landing of the staircase. His arms were folded, his elbows on his knees. One hand dangled between his knees, holding a gun. As if in slow motion, the man raised the pistol at the detective. Haynes fired two times. Both bullets struck a board in the white fence, continued through the wood pile, and struck the suspect in the upper right chest. The man fell backward to the ground.

After the gunshots, officers in the area ran back to the alley. Haynes and the next officer to arrive pulled the man out from under the staircase and rendered first aid. The ambulance had arrived for Detective Cooley, but since Cooley had been taken to the hospital in the police car, the ambulance transported the suspect to Memorial Hospital where armed robbery suspect Christopher Flener was pronounced dead on arrival.

THIRTEEN

CHIEF THOMAS HAD called Sergeant Nealis into his office the second week of September.

"How is Carroll Cooley doing since his shooting?"

"His recovery is slow but sure, Chief. He does have a concern, though."

"He does? What would that be?"

"Well, you know he's sitting number one on the sergeants list."

"Yes, he is," Chief Thomas said.

"Well, he's afraid if he doesn't get back to work, and if you need somebody to fill the position, well...that you might pass him over."

The chief thought for a moment and said, "If he feels up to it, have Cooley call my secretary and make an appointment to see me."

Nealis went to his office and picked up his telephone. "Hey, Carroll, you feel well enough to come down to the station?"

"Sure, Sarge, whaddaya got?" Cooley mumbled.

"The chief wants to see ya."

"Oh crap, what's the chief want to see me for?"

CARROLL COOLEY HAD come into police work after doing a hitch in the Air Force. He applied to the Phoenix Police Department in January of 1958. He waited through February. March came, and he still hadn't received word.

Then he read in the newspaper that the Phoenix Police Department was hiring a new academy class in April. Cooley wondered why he hadn't been called. He told his wife, Glee, that he was going to the police station to check on his application status and he headed downtown.

There, Cooley complained to the chief's secretary, Lillian Ward. Lillian was polite, diplomatic, and competent. She was also the sister of Assistant Chief Ward.

"The academy schedule for April is full, Mr. Cooley. You should just wait for the next one."

Cooley's lips tightened and his hands went to his hips. "No," he said.

"Would you mind waiting a minute while I look up the paperwork for the academy classes? Stay right here—it'll only take a minute."

Cooley waited in the outer office, pacing back and forth. He rubbed his chin and cupped his elbow with his other hand.

Lillian returned with the class roster. "Yes," she said, then paused to clear her throat. "Here's your name, Carroll Cooley, and it's underlined. That means you were scheduled as an alternate in the January class. See right here, your name is underlined."

Cooley leaned over, looked at his name, and straightened back up. "What does that mean?"

"Well, it means," said Lillian patiently, "that if someone had dropped out of the current class or didn't show up for the first day, you would have been called to go to the Police Academy in their place."

"Did anyone drop out?" Cooley asked.

"No," Lillian said, "everyone showed up the first day. Some have dropped out since, but after the first day we don't put in alternates."

She paused. Cooley simmered.

"The next class starts in a few weeks, after the April class begins. Maybe we can schedule you for that class."

"This is unacceptable," Cooley said. "I should have been the first person selected in the class starting in April."

Lillian saw she was not going to be able to reason with the

angry man. "Did you want to see Chief Thomas?"

Cooley paused and thought about the stranger in the office on the other side of the door. *He's just a figurehead of a city department. What've I got to lose?* "Yes. Yes, I would."

Cooley again paced the floor while the secretary spoke to the chief. Cooley's anger rose as he thought about the jobs he had turned down while waiting for the call to go to the Phoenix Police Academy. The chief was now being briefed about his predicament. How would he convince this man he needed this job?

Cooley had dropped out of Phoenix Union High School to join the Navy with his buddy. But the Navy had a six-month wait list, so the two boys didn't sign up. Cooley decided he wasn't going to go back to high school. He got a job as a stocker at the Dale Drug Store, at Central and Broadway. Then he jockeyed cars at Rudolph Chevrolet. Eventually he quit that job and went with three of his buddies to hitchhike across the United States.

After returning from their adventure, Cooley and his friends joined the Air Force. Cooley made rank and became a skilled electrician. He married and had two young children. Nothing he had done in his life, thus far, made him an exceptional candidate for police work, but he needed a job to feed his family and to pay the rent. If the police department didn't hire him, he would try to rejoin the Air Force.

Lillian opened the chief's door and left it standing open. "Chief Thomas will see you now, Mr. Cooley."

Cooley stepped into the chief's office. His lips were tight. The muscles in his neck constricted and he swallowed hard.

Chief Thomas looked up from his reading. "What do you want?"

Cooley didn't hold back. "Chief, I have a wife and two young children to feed. I applied for the academy class that started in January and I was told I would be called." Cooley paused and took a breath. "I turned down other jobs so I wouldn't have to quit them when this one came through. And I waited as patiently as I could. Then I read the newspaper this morning and it said the police were hiring an academy class for April. I'm mad that I wasn't called, and I came down here to see what was going on."

The chief remained seated and spoke in a calm, firm voice. "You can attend the Police Academy that's starting in a few weeks."

"I can't wait a few weeks," Cooley said, "for the reasons I just stated."

Chief Thomas held up the paper he had been reading. "This is the class roster for the April class. I only have so many seats." He paused, looked at Cooley. Cooley didn't flinch. "I guess I can add one more."

Cooley said nothing.

"You report to the Police Academy on Monday morning," Chief Thomas said. "And Cooley, if you're late, don't bother going in."

CARROLL COOLEY NOW sat in the chief's outer office and wiped his sweaty palms on the thighs of his trousers. It had been four weeks since he'd been shot in the face. He gently touched the star shaped wound on his right upper lip. He didn't realize he'd been shot at the time. He'd heard an explosion in his head, he'd spit out a tooth, and then the hot blood gushed from his mouth.

Later, it occurred to him that the bullet had fragmented into pieces, causing a burning sensation. The pain had run along the path of the bullet that tore the flesh under the skin from his mouth and passed over his cheek bone. The largest piece of the bullet lodged above his right ear. Now when he spoke it sounded like he was talking around a mouth full of marbles.

Chief Charlie Thomas had the reputation as a great guy, a cop's cop, firm and fair. He was also tough, a disciplinarian—and officers tensed up in his presence. Cooley had spent five years working under Chief Thomas, who was in his tenth year as Phoenix's top cop. The chief had built a legacy of courage, integrity, and vision that reshaped the department.

Cooley tried to figure out just why he was so nervous, easily agitated, and anxious. It was out of character for him. He shifted in his seat and wrung his hands again. He was just waiting to see the chief, right?

Charlie Thomas became the chief of police in 1952, chosen over two dozen other applicants. He'd been a probationary lieutenant and they'd skipped him up a couple ranks to make him the police chief. He'd taken the job knowing the department had gone through twenty-six chiefs in the previous twenty-five years.

When Thomas became chief he served notice that the corruption and lack of professionalism that had plagued the department for years was going to change. He modeled himself after his former partner and mentor, T. R. "Lefty" Mofford. Then he blazed a trail, giving Phoenix a reputation for a tough, fair, and professional police department. Thomas made policies, held officers to them, and backed those policies with tough, no-nonsense training and monitoring of that training.

His white sidewall haircut complemented his relatively coarse features. His keen eyes held a direct gaze—watchful, the kind of look men have after they've spent a lot of time being ready for trouble and have dealt effectively with whatever situations came their way. Thomas coupled quick wits, good verbal skills, and a well-controlled temper with a voice that projected calm and reassurance.

Charlie Thomas didn't hide in his office and delegate authority. He could be seen during the day, walking through the different bureaus, speaking to civilians and officers of all ranks. He had a phenomenal memory and knew everyone on the department by name.

As chief, he appointed the first black sergeant. He placed a black officer on a beat in a white neighborhood and then stood by him through the public criticism and death threats made to both men.

He moved women out of "meter maid" status, sent them to the Police Academy, and put seven regular, sworn female officers on walking beats in downtown. Thomas expected his officers to be better educated, act intelligently on the job, and be mentally and physically fit.

Okay, Cooley thought, *that's why I'm scared...I'm sitting here with a hole in my face, and I mumble when I try to talk.*

Carroll Cooley wasn't sure why the chief wanted to talk to him. Cooley had mentioned to Sergeant Nealis that he felt that he wasn't recovering fast enough. He had taken the test for promotion from detective to sergeant and had placed third on the list, right behind

Robert Kornegay and Dave Lozier. Kornegay and Lozier had already been promoted. Resting at home, on the mend, Cooley told Nealis he thought he might be passed over while sitting at the number one spot on the promotion list. He was apprehensive that he might not be considered "physically fit."

Cooley wrung his hands and looked around the chief's lobby for what felt like the hundredth time. He replayed everything in his mind—the conversations with Nealis, the chief's history. It had been five years since Cooley had been in the chief's office. Chief Thomas was no longer a stranger or just the figurehead of a city department. This time Cooley couldn't talk to the chief as he had before—as if he had nothing to lose.

Now he could only wait for the chief to tell him he wasn't fit for duty—that he wasn't eligible to be a police sergeant.

"Detective Cooley," Lillian said, "the chief will see you now."

The chief stood up when Cooley entered the room. "Come in, Carroll, have a seat. Tell me how you're recovering." The chief gestured to a chair in front of his mahogany desk. The two men sat down, facing each other.

"Well, Chief, I had some dental work done," Cooley said, as distinctly as he could. "And I'm healing up pretty well."

"Did they get the bullet out?"

"No...the bullet damaged some teeth." Cooley pointed at the entry point on his right upper lip. "It entered here, took out this tooth, and then it fragmented into my nasal cavity. The largest piece of the bullet traveled below my eye, around my cheekbone, and lodged by my right ear. The doctors didn't want to remove the remainder of the bullet. They felt an operation would cause more harm than good." Cooley turned his head, leaned in toward the chief and touched his index finger to the small lump by his right ear. "I can feel it right here."

"Do the doctors expect you to fully recover?"

"Oh yes, sir. They tell me it'll just take a little time." Cooley wiped his lower lip and chin in case there was any spittle.

Chief Thomas leaned forward and laced his fingers together on the desk. "So what's this bunk I hear about you not thinking I'll promote you to sergeant?"

Cooley looked at the chief and stammered, "I...I...didn't say that, Chief." Cooley looked down at his hands. "Uh, you know, Chief, I, ah, still sound like I can't talk right and..."

"You listen to me, Cooley. I put you on that sergeant's list for a reason, and I don't see why I shouldn't promote you before that list expires...that is, unless you don't think you're fit for the position."

"No I'll be okay by then...fit for duty, sir."

"Then you better go home and get well. And I don't want hear anything more about this, you understand me?"

"Yes, Chief, I understand."

OCTOBER 9, 1963, Chief Thomas promoted Carroll Cooley to the rank of sergeant. Cooley would be part of the Phoenix Police Department's response in 1966, when Ernest Miranda reappeared on the scene, courtesy of the U.S. Supreme Court.

FOURTEEN

ALVIN MOORE, ERNEST Miranda's court-appointed attorney, appealed his client's case to the Arizona Supreme Court on April 22, 1965, on the grounds that Miranda's constitutional right to legal counsel in the Margaret Fair case had been denied.

The Arizona Supreme Court quickly ruled that Miranda's conviction for the kidnap and rape of Margaret Fair would be upheld for two main reasons. First, there was no legal requirement at the time of the arrest for Miranda to be advised of his right to counsel. Second, Miranda hadn't asked for an attorney to assist him or to represent him at the time police questioned him. The judge ruled the case would have to be appealed to the next level.

Alvin Moore was seventy-five years old and unable to continue the appeal process because of his failing health. Attorney Robert J. Corcoran of the American Civil Liberties Union (ACLU) asked criminal defense attorney John J. Flynn to represent Miranda pro bono. Flynn's partner, John P. Frank, assisted Flynn, along with associate Peter D. Baird from the law firm of Lewis and Roca in Phoenix. Together, the lawyers wrote a 2,500-word "petition for certiorari," arguing that Miranda's Fifth Amendment rights had been violated, and submitted it to the United States Supreme Court.

When the Supreme Court received the "petition for certiorari," they were already reviewing several other cases involving civil rights violations of persons placed under arrest.

From 1961 through the better part of 1965, the United States Supreme Court reviewed the following cases, all of them pertaining to the rights of suspects:

Mapp v. Ohio, 1961: a Fourth Amendment issue which protects against unreasonable searches and seizures.

Gideon v. Wainwright, 1963: A Fourteenth Amendment issue, where the Supreme Court unanimously ruled that state courts are required to provide counsel in criminal cases to represent defendants who are unable to afford to pay their own attorneys.

Escobedo v. Illinois, 1964: The Sixth Amendment guarantees the right to legal counsel at all significant stages of a criminal proceeding. The Supreme Court determined that a suspect has the right to have counsel present during police questioning and/or for a suspect to consult with an attorney before being questioned by police. This applied when the police intended to use the answers given by the suspect against them at a trial. It also applied if the person being questioned was being detained and questioned against their will.

In addition, the United States Supreme Court also handed down the "Fundamentals of Fairness Standard," applicable at both the state and federal level. The Court believed this standard would uphold constitutional guarantees of due process for the accused. With this standard, the Supreme Court sent a clear signal to law enforcement and criminal justice officials that convictions not made in conformity with the Fundamentals of Fairness Standard would likely be overturned.

The United States Supreme Court agreed to review the Miranda case, along with three other cases involving custodial interrogations, during the Court's October 1965 term.

1. *Miranda v. Arizona.*
2. *Michael Vignera v. State of New York.*
3. *Carl Calvin Westover v. United States.*
4. *California v. Roy Alan Stewart.*

In each of these cases, police officers, detectives, or a prosecuting attorney conducted interviews in a room in where the defendant was cut off from the outside world when questioned. In none of these cases was the defendant given a full and effective warning of his rights at the outset of the interrogation process. In each of these cases, the questioning drew out oral admissions from the suspect, and, in three of the cases, the suspects signed statements which were later admitted at their trials.

The Supreme Court Justices deliberations would be based on the following information:

Miranda v. Arizona: The court determined that Miranda was officially under arrest at the time police picked up Miranda at his home and took him to the police station. A witness identified Miranda at the station. Police officers then interrogated him for two hours. The result was a signed written confession. Prosecutors subsequently presented Miranda's oral and written confessions to the jury. The jury found Miranda guilty of kidnapping and rape. He was sentenced to twenty to thirty years imprisonment on each count. On appeal, the Supreme Court of Arizona held that Miranda's constitutional rights had not been violated in obtaining the confession.

Vignera v. New York: Officers of the New York Police Department picked up Vignera in connection with the robbery of a dress shop that had occurred three days prior. NYPD took Vignera to the 17th Precinct detective squad headquarters. He was moved to the 66th detective squad, where he orally admitted to the robbery and was placed under arrest. NYPD shipped Vignera to the 70th Precinct for detention, where he was questioned by an assistant district attorney. A hearing reporter stood by, transcribing the questions and answers. Prosecutors presented both Vignera's oral confession and the transcript to the jury. Vignera was found guilty of first-degree robbery and sentenced to thirty to sixty years imprisonment. The Appellate Division and the Court of Appeals affirmed the conviction without opinion.

Westover v. United States: Police in Kansas City, Missouri, arrested Carl Calvin Westover for several local robberies. Money was found in Westover's pocket. The numbers on some of the currency jibed with some of the numbers on the bait money handed to the robber at the Bank of America, a federally insured bank in Sacramento, California. The FBI became involved.

At the police station, the FBI informed Kansas City police that Westover was also wanted on a felony charge in California. Police officers interrogated Westover on the night of the arrest and the next morning, when they obtained a signed confession. The FBI agents then interrogated Westover. While the local police did not inform Westover of his rights, the FBI did. After two-and-a-half hours, Westover signed separate confessions for the two robberies in California. One of the agents wrote down Westover's confessions during the interrogation and had Westover sign them. These statements were introduced at trial and Westover was convicted of the California robberies. He was sentenced to fifteen years imprisonment on each count. The Court of Appeals for the Ninth Circuit affirmed the conviction. The Supreme Court reviewed the case and agreed with the Ninth Circuit Court's decision.

California v. Stewart: Police arrested Roy Alan Stewart at his home, along with Stewart's wife and three other adults, in connection with a series of purse-snatch robberies. One of the victims had died of injuries inflicted by her assailant. A store owner identified Stewart as the endorser of checks stolen in one of the robberies. Stewart was placed in a cell and, over the next five days, officers interrogated him on nine different occasions. During the ninth interrogation session, Stewart admitted that he had robbed the deceased woman. He said he didn't mean to hurt her. Police released the four other people arrested with Stewart because there was no evidence to connect them to the crimes. During the trial, Stewart's statements were introduced, and he was convicted of robbery and first-degree murder. Stewart was sentenced to death. The Supreme Court of California reversed the decision, holding that Stewart should have been advised of his right to remain silent and to his right to counsel.

The Supreme Court determined the issues were, first, whether "statements obtained from an individual who is subjected to custodial police interrogation" are admissible against him in a criminal trial. And second, whether "procedures which assure that the individual is accorded his privilege under the Fifth Amendment to the Constitution not to be compelled to incriminate himself" are necessary.

The Supreme Court held that:

> *"There can be no doubt that the Fifth Amendment privilege is available outside of criminal court proceedings and serves to protect persons in all settings in which their freedom of action is curtailed in any significant way from being compelled to incriminate themselves."* As such, *"the prosecution may not use statements, whether exculpatory or inculpatory, stemming from custodial interrogation of the defendant unless it demonstrates the use of procedural safeguards effective to secure the privilege against self-incrimination.*
>
> *"By custodial interrogation, we mean questioning initiated by law enforcement officers after a person has been taken into custody or otherwise deprived of his freedom of action in any significant way."*

The Supreme Court further held that:

> *"Without proper safeguards the process of in-custody interrogation of persons suspected or accused of crime contains inherently compelling pressures which work to undermine the individual's will to resist and to compel him to speak where he would otherwise do so freely."*
>
> Therefore, a defendant *"must be warned prior to any questioning that he has the right to remain silent, that anything he says can be used against him in a court of law, that he has the right to the presence of an attorney, and that if he cannot afford an attorney one will be appointed for him prior to any questioning if he so desires."*

The Supreme Court argued the issues involving: *Miranda v. Arizona; Michael Vignera v. State of New York; Carl Calvin Westover v. United States, and California v. Roy Alan Stewart.*

Arguments began on February 28, 1966, and ran through March 2, 1966. The Supreme Court reached a decision on June 13, 1966, in a vote of 5-4.

The Supreme Court reversed the judgments of the Supreme Court of Arizona in the Miranda case, the New York Court of Appeals in the Vignera case, and the Court of Appeals for the Ninth

Circuit in the Westover case, and affirmed the judgment of the Supreme Court of California in the Stewart case.

Chief Justice Earl Warren wrote the majority opinion. He was joined by justices Black, Douglas, Brennan, and Fortas. Justice Harlan wrote the dissenting opinion. Justices Stewart and White sided with Harlan, along with Justice Clark, who wrote some of the dissenting opinion. Because *Miranda v. Arizona* was the first case listed, the judgment became known as the "Miranda Decision." The so-called Miranda Warning was to be implemented by police departments and officers of the court.

The Phoenix Police Department, in cooperation with the Maricopa County Attorney's Office, would elect to use a business-card-size form that officers could carry in their pocket and read aloud to suspects so that there would be no misunderstanding of the suspect's Miranda Rights. At the bottom of the card, they added the words: DO YOU UNDERSTAND THESE RIGHTS? And, WILL YOU VOLUNTARILY ANSWER MY QUESTIONS? They designed the card with spaces for the officer to write the date, the Departmental Report Number, abbreviated DR#, and the Officer's initials, abbreviated as OFF INITIALS.

Over the years, the form developed into form PPD #29, with its latest revision occurring in May of 1998. The front of the card is written in English. The back is written in Spanish. The front of the card reads:

> ·YOU HAVE THE RIGHT TO REMAIN SILENT.
> ·ANYTHING YOU SAY CAN BE USED AGAINST YOU IN COURT OF LAW.
> ·YOU HAVE THE RIGHT TO THE PRESENCE OF AN ATTORNEY TO ASSIST YOU PRIOR TO QUESTIONING, AND TO BE WITH YOU DURING QUESTIONING, IF YOU SO DESIRE.
> ·IF YOU CANNOT AFFORD AN ATTORNEY YOU HAVE THE RIGHT TO HAVE AN ATTORNEY APPOINTED FOR YOU PRIOR TO QUESTIONING.
> ·DO YOU UNDERSTAND THESE RIGHTS?
> ·WILL YOU VOLUNTARILY ANSWER MY QUESTIONS?
> ·DATE: DR#:   OFF INITIALS:

FIFTEEN

WHEN THE U.S. Supreme Court reversed the Arizona Supreme Court's judgment against Ernest Miranda for his crimes against Margaret Fair on June 13, 1966, the case attracted national attention. Law enforcement agencies around the entire country would now be legally obligated to adhere to the Miranda Rights prior to the interrogation of suspects.

Miranda's 1963 conviction in the Barbara McDaniel trial had not been included in attorney Alvin Moore's appeal to the Arizona Supreme Court—nor was it included in attorney John J. Flynn's appeal to the United States Supreme Court. Therefore, the guilty verdict in the McDaniel case remained unaffected by the U.S. Supreme Court's ruling in the Margaret Fair case.

In 1966, Ernie Miranda was still serving the twenty to thirty-year prison sentence he had received in the McDaniel case.

The Supreme Court's decision returned the Miranda case involving Margaret Fair to the Maricopa County Superior Court for a retrial. Miranda's confession had been ruled inadmissible. The trial would now be based on evidence and testimony. Maricopa County Attorney Robert Corbin and his chief deputy, Maurice Berger, took personal charge of the prosecution. Detective Cooley had since been promoted to sergeant and was assigned to assist in preparing the case. The County Attorney's office completed a thorough review of the evidence and the possible witnesses.

TWILA HOFFMAN HAD been living with Ernie since 1962. When Ernie went to prison in 1963, Twila moved to Chandler, Arizona with her three children. In 1966, she was still living in Chandler and worked as a desk aid at Mesa General Hospital. Although he was still in prison at this time, Ernie was suing her for custody of their daughter.

Sergeant Cooley and prosecutors Robert Corbin and Maurice Berger arranged to question her in the hospital lobby about acting as a witness in the retrial of Ernest Miranda.

"What is your relationship to Ernest Miranda?" Corbin asked.

"Ernie is my common-law husband."

"Did you visit Ernest while he was in jail?"

"I visited Ernie at the county jail when he was awaiting his first trials. Then I saw him again at the county jail for his latest trials here in the Superior Court."

"When you visited Ernest, did he ever you tell you whether he committed the crimes he was accused of? Did he deny the charges against him?" Corbin asked.

"Well, the last time I went to see Ernie, he said that he did force the girl into his car and drove out to a place in the desert and raped her."

"Did he say anything else?"

"Ernie said the only way he could win the next trial would be to marry the girl. I became upset. He went on to say we were not really married, so he could marry her. Then, as his wife, the girl couldn't testify against him, ever."

"What did you tell Ernie?" Corbin asked.

"I started crying, and I told him it wouldn't work, that he was married to me. He said it would work. He wanted me to take our baby and go see her. He wanted me to tell her that if she wouldn't testify against Ernie at his trial, he would marry her when he got out of jail."

"Would you be willing to testify to this conversation at Ernie's new trial?" Corbin asked.

"Yeah, but you gotta understand that I don't have any ill

feelings toward Ernie. I don't want no revenge."

Twila Hoffman was then placed on the list of witnesses to testify for the prosecution.

ERNEST MIRANDA'S NEW trial for the Margaret Fair rape case was initially set for October of 1966. The prosecution delayed the trial until February 15, 1967, because Margaret Fair was now married and pregnant. Her baby would be born at the end of 1966.

The State of Arizona held the trial in Judge Lawrence K. Wren's courtroom. Due to Miranda's notoriety, the court presented him with an alias of Jose Gomez instead of his real name. The trial lasted seven days. The attorneys spent a lot of time arguing various motions before the judge, most of it outside the presence of the jury.

One important argument centered on the admissibility of Twila Hoffman's testimony. The question arose: was Hoffman's conversation with Miranda a privileged communication in the rule of law that prevented a wife from testifying against her husband? Judge Wren ruled that Miranda's confession to Ms. Hoffman was not privileged information, since Arizona didn't recognize common-law marriages as being legal.

The judge ruled Margaret Fair's identification of Ernest Miranda inadmissible on the grounds that she had not been completely positive when she initially viewed the live lineup. Nevertheless, the jury found Ernest Miranda guilty of Kidnapping and Rape a second time. He was sentenced in the second week of June 1967, nearly one year to the day after Chief Justice Earl Warren, speaking for the 5-4 deciding majority, established unequivocal guidelines about what is and what is not permissible in the interrogation room.

SIXTEEN

ABOUT 1:00 P.M., Saturday, January 31, 1976, Ernie Miranda stepped through the door of the La Amapola bar. He'd been out of prison for a month and was staying with his brother Ruben. Ernie stood under the illuminated wall clock that hung above the door as his eyes adjusted to the light. Cigarette smoke filled the establishment all the way to the ceiling. The air reeked of stale beer and acrid tobacco. A whiff of vomit completed the effect.

Ernie moved past the people shooting pool at two tables in the middle of the barroom. He glanced at the light suspended on chains above the tables. A jukebox, barely visible through the smoke, sat against one wall. Ernie momentarily focused on the song, the bolero-styled "Tristeza."

Ernie walked the length of the bar to sit on the second stool from the end, near the pass through. He thought he blended in with the other patrons in his unkempt blue and white print shirt, blue pants, and dirty white loafers.

The bartender, twenty-four-year-old Sophia Cortez, knew Ernie as one of the locals who drifted in and out of the area bars in the Deuce. She smiled and served him a cold bottle of Coors. Sophia then issued him a well-used deck of playing cards because most of the men played poker, gambling their change while at the bar.

Ernie liked both the La Amapola and the Nogales bars. They

were a block apart and had the same owner. Ernie never asked why the old man had named the bars with the Spanish words for "poppy" and "walnuts."

Sophia opened a second beer and served it to her friend, twenty-one-year-old Catalina Gomez, who sat on the barstool next to Ernie. The two women watched over the shoulders of Ernie and Sophia's boyfriend, twenty-four-year-old Fernando Rodriguez, play cards with another young man. A lit cigarette hung from Ernie's lips as he shuffled and dealt to the two other men. Both were more than ten years his junior. *Patsies*, Ernie thought.

Sophia's younger half-sister, twenty-one-year-old Adelina Hidalgo, shot pool with her boyfriend, Manuel Vasquez, also known as "Chapo." Adelina also tended bar at La Amapola. She was due to come on duty at 6:00 p.m.

Adelina glanced over at the bar, where a small crowd of customers sat under a large cloud of cigarette smoke. An older man, passed out drunk, slumped on the first stool by the door, leaning against the wall. What caught Adelina's attention was how the man remained perched without falling. The stools were attached to the bar at the footrest. Otherwise, she reasoned, the stool would have slid out from under him. "I wouldn't allow a drunk to sleep in the bar if I was on duty," Adelina playfully told Sophia.

"You mind your own business, *chica*," Sophia said, laughing. She then told her card-playing boyfriend, Fernando, that she needed his help at the other end of the bar. Sophia and Adelina tried to wake up the old man by shaking him. Sophia even poured a glass of water on him. Fernando shook the man, and noticed a yellow-handled knife protruding from the man's back pocket. Fernando took the folding knife, opened it, and looked at the hook in the blade.

It was a lettuce knife, the kind used by workers in the lettuce fields. Fernando closed the knife and put it in his own pocket. Adelina saw Fernando take the knife from the sleeping man and shook her head. Then she grabbed the man's warm beer and poured it on him.

"He's not going to wake up," Fernando said. "Let him sleep."

Adelina decided not to spend the afternoon in the bar. She motioned to Chapo that she wanted to leave. They waived at Sophia and left the bar.

Business slowed through the afternoon in the La Amapola. During the lulls, Ernie watched Sophia clean glasses, empty ashtrays, and wipe the bar. When she wasn't doing chores she came out from behind the bar and shot pool.

Ernie continued playing cards with Sophia's boyfriend, Fernando, and the other man—twenty-three-year-old Eseziquel Moreno. Moreno and Fernando downed beer after beer. Ernie nursed his bottles of Coors. He was sure no one noticed he was cheating at cards.

After several hours, the two younger men were drunk. Ernie had only a buzz and he was still winning. All three men spoke in Spanish and their voices would sometimes rise over the music from the jukebox, echoes bouncing off the walls of the smoky barroom. Sophia watched them to be sure their drinking and penny ante bets didn't get out of hand.

Adelina and Chapo returned to the bar just after 5:30 p.m., a half-hour before Adelina's shift started. They shot pool to pass the time. Sophia had already stopped working. She sat at the bar next to Catalina. They each had a beer.

Adelina edged around the pool table, lining up a shot, and taking the opportunity to check on the men playing cards. She watched Fernando clumsily lift a bottle of Coors to his mouth and take a long pull. His shirt came up, showing the outline of the knife in the pocket of his light blue pants. *Fernando still has the knife he took from the drunk.* Adelina went behind the bar and Chapo continued to shoot pool.

It was just after 6:00 p.m. Fernando threw his cards on the bar. "You're cheating us, Ernie," Fernando said, in slurred Spanish.

"No, you took three dollars from the pot, *ese*," Ernie responded.

"Moreno has the money," Fernando said, as he took nearly three dollars in change from the bar in front of Moreno. Using the edge of his hand to slide the money off the bar, Fernando pushed the change into his cupped hand at the bar's edge and threw the money into the pot, "There's your money, *ese*."

"No, it won't be done that way." Ernie said.

Adelina saw the commotion and yelled at the men to stop

arguing. They ignored her and jumped off their bar stools. Ernie quickly punched Moreno in the face. Moreno fell back against the wall and collapsed to the floor. Ernie squared off with Fernando and struck a flurry of punches to his face and forehead. Fernando's knees wobbled. He tried to swing his half-closed fists. The beer had taken its toll. Fernando couldn't land a fist on Ernie.

Adelina came from behind the bar and wedged a hip between the two men, pinning them against the barstools that were solidly bolted to the base of the bar. "Stop fighting or I'll call the cops." She glared at them, her lips in a tight thin line. She jerked her head from one man to the other. "No more beer and no more cards."

Adelina returned behind the bar, her chest heaving. She aimed a dirty look at Chapo, who was amusing himself at the pool table. He had kept shooting pool while she'd faced down two angry drunks. Chapo saw Adelina looking at him. He laid his cue stick on the table and raised his open hands at his sides, chest high. He lifted his chin and said in a voice loud enough for her to hear, "What do you want from me?" He laughed and continued to shoot pool. Adelina shook her head and half smiled.

Moreno bled from an old cut on his nose that had reopened when Ernie punched him. Fernando had a reddened forehead, smeared with blood, along with a swollen face and a split lower lip. He wiped his bloody chin on his sleeve, smearing more blood on his cheeks.

Adelina left the ashtray the men had been using on the bar, but put the playing cards away in a drawer, and started dragging empty beer bottles off the bar. Ernie scraped the small pot of change off the bar and shoved the ill-gotten money into his front pants pocket.

"You can come behind the bar and wash the blood off your hands," Adelina said. When he joined her behind the bar she leaned close and warned Ernie, "Fernando is upset, and he has a knife." She hoped Ernie would heed the warning and leave the bar.

"I don't care if he has a knife," Ernie said, and, in a huff, he disappeared into the bathroom to wash the blood off his hands there.

While Ernie was gone, Fernando helped Moreno to his feet. The two men spoke but couldn't be heard over the jukebox.

Fernando wobbled backwards a step, pulled the knife out of his pocket, and said to Moreno in a loud voice, "Here, you finish it, finish the fight."

When Ernie walked out of the bathroom, Fernando was at the first pool table holding a cue stick. Sophia slapped Fernando on the arm and said, "We have to leave. Let's get out of here."

Moreno was waiting at the bar. He had recovered from the punch in the face. He hadn't been ready when Ernie hit him, and now he wanted revenge.

Ernie felt confident. He'd won the fight against his two younger opponents. He had beaten them at cards and he had almost three extra dollars in his pocket to prove it.

Moreno's arms were rigid at his sides, his fists clenched so tight they shook. He leered at Ernie through the smoke.

"You *puto*, you cheated," Moreno shouted over the music on the jukebox. "You took our money."

Ernie didn't respond.

"You punched me when I wasn't ready, *ese*," Moreno said, moving closer to Ernie. "Come on, *pendejo*, I'll fight you now." Spittle sprayed from Moreno's mouth.

Ernie said, "I beat you with one punch and you lost, man. I beat both of you."

Moreno's jaw tightened and his teeth clenched. He dug the yellow-handled knife out of his pants pocket and began to open the folded blade. He broadened his stance, tugged some more, and the blade clicked in place.

"You don't need a knife, *ese*, you got beat."

"You cheated," Moreno said. "Now you'll pay."

Ernie grabbed for the knife and the two men clinched. They spread their feet apart and an awkward dance began. They rocked side to side a few times before Moreno freed his right hand and thrust all four inches of the knife blade into the left side of Ernie's stomach. Ernie grabbed at Moreno's knife hand. The hook at the end of the blade tore at Ernie's insides. Their crab-like dance carried the two men over to the pool table closest to the bar. The people in the bar turned to watch.

Moreno's face contorted with rage. He pulled the knife out,

ripping even more of Ernie's flesh. Moreno twisted Ernie's arm with one hand, kept a tight grip on the knife with the other, and pointed the knife at Ernie's chest. Ernie squirmed but he couldn't keep the blade from being driven its length into his chest. The blade went between his ribs and into his left lung, nicking his heart. He gasped.

Ernie's grip on Moreno's knife hand slackened, and he crumpled to the floor. Moreno jerked the knife out of Ernie's chest and rested a bloody hand on a pocket of the pool table. The Mexican music continued to blare from the jukebox. Moreno realized the few patrons left in the bar were staring at him. Feeling the impact of what he'd done, Moreno fled through the curtain of cigarette smoke and out the west entrance of the La Amapola.

Adelina ran to the doorway and watched Moreno run north on 2nd Street, then east through the alley behind Madison. She turned to Ernie who lay in a clump on the dirty cement floor by the pool table. He had pulled himself into a fetal position, motionless except for his labored breathing.

"ONE, TWO, THREE, lift." The ambulance attendants moved Ernie from the floor to a gurney. The pain in his chest and stomach was excruciating. He couldn't breathe and he couldn't move. He could only lie there, smelling stale beer, cigarette smoke, and a whiff of vomit. They rushed him to Good Samaritan Hospital.

SEVENTEEN

OFFICERS GARY BARTON and John Williams were on foot patrol, walking in the evening shadows on Jefferson Street between 1st and 2nd streets. They made small talk between the minor incidents and skirmishes that occurred on their beat in the Deuce.

When their stroll brought them to 2nd Street, they glanced to the south at about the same time and saw a Phoenix Fire Truck and a Universal Ambulance at the La Amapola bar. The emergency vehicles were surrounded by a crowd gathered on the sidewalk at the bar's entrance. The ambulance was leaving, rolling northbound with lights on and siren screaming.

The officers broke into a jog, arrived at the scene, and started asking bystanders what had happened. Most of the patrons wouldn't answer the cops' questions. Williams talked to firemen who had responded from Phoenix Fire Station #1, a block away, at 1st Street and Jefferson. Officer Barton found a bystander who would talk. The man, a short Hispanic with disheveled hair, wore a dirty white tank top and blue jeans. The man looked all around before speaking to Barton, while keeping his hands in his front pockets.

"I just barely got here, man."

"Well, what happened when you first got here?" Barton asked.

"Some guy got stabbed in the Amapola."

"When?"

"About a half hour ago. An ambulance just took him to the hospital, man."

"Did you see who did it?"

"Nah, man, probably another Mexican." The man shrugged and then walked away when Officer Williams joined Barton.

"The firemen said a Mexican male was stabbed. Universal Ambulance took him to Good Sam. The stabbing happened about six o'clock," Williams said.

The two officers secured the crime scene by locking the door of the La Amapola's 2nd Street main entrance. Their initial check inside the bar revealed only a puddle of blood next to one of the pool tables.

"Looks like the ambulance guys did a scoop and run," Williams said. "I'll secure the back door."

"Okay I'll try to find a witness," Barton said. "Hopefully, someone who speaks English."

Reliable witnesses would be few to none. Those who spoke English may have had negative contacts with the Phoenix Police and wouldn't talk to them. Those who didn't speak English would need a Spanish-speaking officer to translate. Others were undocumented Mexican nationals, and they would want nothing to do with the police.

After all, this was "the Deuce," Phoenix's skid row. The Deuce ran from the railroad tracks south of Jackson Street, north to Washington, and centered around 2nd Street. When asked why they called this area the Deuce, veteran and retired Phoenix officers would give a couple of different answers. One version claimed that the Deuce was the walking-beat area in the section of town where trains off-loaded produce into warehouses and the name was a shortened form of "produce." Another explanation claimed it was a tough area to work, and "deuce" meant "something difficult or bad." The most probable reason was that the Deuce centered around 2nd Street.

Some officers liked working in the Deuce because it had a history stemming out of Prohibition. In those days the area was known for speakeasies, brothels, and gambling houses lined along 2nd Street and continuing down Jefferson and Washington streets.

Over time, the Deuce became an area dominated by one-story buildings housing bars and pawnshops. The few two-story buildings were small hotels. In 1976, the Deuce was still a tougher part of the city. Farm laborers hung out there to socialize or shoot pool, along with a mix of dope dealers, hookers, and vagrants.

Working in the Deuce built both character and an officer's reputation for having the ability to deal with people from different walks of life—and with various types of crimes, typically involving unusual circumstances. If you could work in the Deuce, you could work anywhere in Phoenix.

The rapport that Phoenix walking-beat officers had with the citizens, the popularity of the victim among his associates, and the seriousness of the crime would determine the amount of cooperation the police would receive. The question was, would anyone talk to the police on this particular stabbing?

Officer Williams continued to secure the crime scene. Officer Banks arrived and located one witness who hadn't left the bar— Adelina Hidalgo. Banks quickly learned that Hidalgo had seen the fight and the stabbing. He took a Form 36 card from his breast pocket and filled out the 3x5-inch card, writing down Hidalgo's name, date of birth, age, and address. He added a synopsis of what she said on the back of the card. Banks informed her that she would have to be interviewed in more detail by detectives. He told her not to talk to anyone about the stabbing.

Officer Barton attempted to locate witnesses who had left the bar but had remained near the front door. Barton saw a young woman on the sidewalk outside the La Amapola. Her hands were pressed to her face and she appeared to be staring at nothing.

"Can you tell me what happened here?" Barton asked.

"They were just playing cards. Then they were fighting. It all happened so fast," Catalina Gomez said.

"Who were they?" Barton slipped a Form 36 card out of his shirt pocket.

"There was an older guy, about thirty-five. The other two guys were playing cards with him."

Barton looked up from his writing. "Tell me about the two other men."

"They were both about twenty-three," Catalina said.

"What was their height and weight, and what were they wearing?"

"One was a Mexican, five-foot-seven, about one hundred and fifty pounds. He had a white shirt with a flower design sewn on it. His pants were light blue, I think."

"And the other guy?"

"Well, uh, he was a Mexican, five-foot-seven, about one hundred and fifty pounds." Catalina realized the information she was giving to the police might get her into trouble. It might lead to the arrest of Fernando Rodriguez, who was Sophia's boyfriend or the arrest of Fernando's friend, Moreno. No one in the Deuce wanted the reputation of being a snitch or to be known as an informant to the police. Her responses became vague. "But I don't know what he was wearing," Catalina said.

"You don't know what he was wearing?"

"No, that's all I remember."

Barton finished up his 36 card. His experience told him that Catalina would offer no more answers, and, if he pressed for answers, she wouldn't assist officers when they needed information in the future. Barton believed that Catalina may have known the second subject and just didn't want to get him into trouble.

Sergeant Risner, along with officers Robert Lee and Gordon Costa, arrived to take over the security of the crime scene. Barton and Banks passed on the information from their 36 cards to the sergeant and the relieving officers. Since Barton and Banks had the information first hand, Sergeant Risner reassigned them to search nearby bars for the suspects.

The officers knew that witnesses' descriptions of suspects were often unreliable, vague, or even deliberately misleading. The additional information gathered would have to be coupled with evidence to prevent false leads and wasted time.

OFFICERS BARTON AND Banks entered the dimly lit Nogales Bar at 29 South 2nd Street, a block north of the La Amapola. After a few seconds of letting their eyes adjust to the light they began looking around. The smells, the smoke, the clientele, and the music blaring from the juke box were reminiscent of the La Amapola. A quick inventory of the patrons and their reactions to the officers' presence would give them a clue as to who to talk to.

Barton fixed his gaze on a Hispanic male sitting at the bar. The guy didn't even look up to see why the festive din had faded to a murmur. The man's clothes were disheveled. He wore light blue pants with a jacket over a dark blue shirt.

Barton stepped over to the woman seated next to the man. Staring at her memorizing her face, at the same time wordlessly telling her to move out of the way, thinking the man next to her was a potential candidate for the stabbing at the La Amapola. The woman, Sophia Cortez, walked away, repeatedly glancing back over her shoulder. Barton leaned in toward the man. "What's your name?"

"Fernando Rodriquez." A sour whiff of alcohol on the man's breath hit the officer's nostrils.

Barton tilted his head back to dodge the stink. "Do you have any identification on you?"

"No."

"Where did you get the dried blood on your forehead and your face?"

Fernando touched his forehead. "I got it in a fight a little while ago at the Amapola."

"Did you have a knife?"

"I had a knife."

Fernando's statements, together with what Adelina Hidalgo had told him, gave Barton enough probable cause to make a lawful arrest for the stabbing at the La Amapola.

Probable cause for an arrest exists when the facts and circumstances within the police officer's knowledge would lead a reasonable person to believe the suspect has committed, is committing, or is about to commit a crime. Probable cause can be reinforced with additional information and lead to a conviction—or it can evaporate and the officer may have to let the suspect go.

"You're under arrest for aggravated assault at the La Amapola," Barton said.

The two officers handcuffed Fernando Rodriquez. Officer

Barton produced a Miranda Warnings card from his right uniform shirt pocket. At 6:53 p.m., he read the card aloud to Rodriquez. Then Barton asked, "Do you understand your rights?"

Fernando said, "Yeah, I understand my rights."

Barton wrote this statement down, along with the date and time, on the Miranda Warnings card, then returned the card to his shirt pocket. Without asking any further questions, the officers escorted their prisoner out of the bar to the street. When they reached the corner of 2nd Street and Jefferson, Banks called the dispatcher from a police call box. "We've got one in custody, 2nd Street and Jefferson, for the 245, at the La Amapola and we need a wagon."

Within minutes, Officer Warren Friederman arrived, driving a paddy wagon. Officer Friederman transported Fernando Rodriquez to police headquarters at 620 West Washington Street.

HOMICIDE SERGEANT GLENN Kenner had just finished dinner at home when he got the call from the desk sergeant. "Hey, Glenn, we've got a stabbing victim from the La Amapola on 2nd Street in the Deuce. He probably won't survive his injuries. Night dicks sent Cal Lash and Bob Nixon over to the La Amapola until your guys get there."

Kenner telephoned detectives Ron Quaife and G. Marcus Aurelius at their homes and had them meet him at the La Amapola. Upon arrival, the team entered the bar and stood under the large lighted clock inside the 2nd Street entrance. Patrol Sergeant Risner briefed the homicide detectives on the known facts of the aggravated assault while all of the detectives took notes.

After the briefing, Sergeant Kenner gave out assignments. The detectives wrote down everyone's assignments so everyone would know who was responsible for each task.

"Quaife, you got the crime scene and then I want you to find out what witness number one, Adelina Hidalgo, the bartender, knows about all this. She gave a lot of information to Officer Banks and she'll need to be re-interviewed. She speaks good English. Keep in mind she's just seen a fight and a stabbing where the victim might die. She's only twenty-one, but Banks says she's tough beyond her years. She did get a little weepy when Banks asked her about the actual stabbing.

"When Quaife is done with that interview, he'll conduct the remaining interviews of witnesses and suspects at the Criminal Investigations Bureau (CIB). Officers Bueno and Hernandez will assist in translating for the Spanish-speaking suspects.

"Of the two suspects the one in custody has been identified as Fernando Zamura Rodriguez. Rodriguez will need to be interviewed also. He's at CIB."

"Nixon," Kenner continued, "you'll have to go to Good Sam hospital, relieve the patrol officer there. Because of your experience working in the Deuce you're more likely to be able to identify the victim."

"Got it, Sarge."

"Marcus," Kenner said, "get with Cal Lash and when you see how the evidence fits the story here, go to Good Sam and see if it's consistent with the victim's injuries. Hopefully, Nixon will have identified the victim and you can do the red tag. Then, Marcus, if he does die, I'll need you to attend the autopsy. It'll probably be scheduled for tomorrow. Check with the Medical Examiner's Office in the morning for a time and keep me informed."

Marcus Aurelius looked up from writing notes. "Will do, Sarge."

Kenner let out a long slow breath. "We've worked several homicides this month. Keep me informed. Let me know if any of 'em are related, and I want to know how many we can clear by arrest. Lieutenant Nealis will want the monthly stats for January's recap on Monday."

OFFICER KENNETH KESSLER arrived at the old Phoenix Good Samaritan Hospital at 1033 East McDowell Road and pulled open the lacquered hardwood door. He walked down the corridor, breathing in the smell of bleach coming off the freshly mopped floor. He no longer noticed the ceiling's mahogany beams or the ornate candelabras that seemed to float above the hallway.

"I've been here too many times," Kessler muttered.

Good Samaritan Hospital had been a marvel of the times when it was built in 1923. The hospital had gone through many changes since then. Originally, it had been called the Arizona Deaconess Hospital. A sign on an easel near the nurses' station featured an artist's conception of the new Good Samaritan Hospital to be built in its place with a completion date sometime in 1978. Kessler thought the design resembled a high-rise building in a Flintstones cartoon.

He could hear the murmur of patients in the emergency waiting room as he moved down the hall. When Kessler reached the nurses station the smell of formaldehyde and antiseptics overcame the smell of bleach. The clock on the wall showed 6:45 p.m. The charge nurse wore her gray hair pulled tight under her white cap. The stripe and its shape let the officer know she had graduated from the University of Arizona's College of Nursing.

She came around the desk and led Kessler down a hallway to the ER waiting room where she spoke to him over the din of patients of all ages, races, and sexes, most of them displaying confusion and anxiety with various injuries and ailments.

"The victim has yet to be identified. He's over here in Treatment Room F162. Dr. Robertson is the ER doctor on duty. You'll have to wait here until he can talk to you."

Kessler peered through the 12x12-inch window in the door of the treatment room. The walls in there blazed white under the fluorescent lights. The tile on the floor shone even whiter. Doctor Robertson and his medical team were working on a Hispanic male who lay on a gurney. Kessler could hear the doctor's muffled voice through the door, giving orders, trying to save the patient's life. There were IV's in both of the man's arms, an endotracheal tube in his airway, and a drainage tube in his left chest. Every thirty seconds someone on the medical team called out the patient's blood pressure.

The team performed both external cardiac massage and pulmonary resuscitation on Ernie Miranda. They worked diligently, as they always did. Together, they fought to save the man's life, regardless of his tattooed arms and legs or troubled past. This team was accustomed to treating the life and death emergencies that came with the violence initiated from the Deuce.

EKG wires attached to white patches were affixed to Ernie's chest. Doctor Robertson feverishly tried to stop the bleeding from the wounds in Miranda's left chest and abdomen. While the IV fluids flowed into Ernie's veins, his own blood flowed out of his wounds.

"I need a blood pressure," the doctor said.

At once, the team stopped working the Ambu bag and the CPR that caused the EKG to reflect a regular pulse.

This work stoppage allowed the nurse to take an accurate blood pressure and the machines to evaluate the patient's true condition. The EKG showed the position of the heart chambers and the presence of any damage to the heart. Air hissed quietly from the blood pressure cuff on Ernie's left arm.

"There's no blood pressure, Doctor," one of the nurses said.

A steady, high-pitched tone from the EKG monitor pierced the air. All eyes went to a green screen divided horizontally by a beam of light that flat lined steadily from left to right.

Kessler moved away from the doors as an orderly rolled a crash cart into the room. The cart held a cardiac monitor and a defibrillator. Team members moved quickly, plugging in and setting up the lifesaving equipment.

The circuitry whined as the defibrillator reached the required volts. Then a beep indicated a primed charge. A shout of "Clear," a jolt, and Ernie's torso jumped and landed back on the gurney. The tone continued to indicate no heartbeat. A second attempt and the same tone sounded. A third attempt once more yielded the same tone. Dr. Robertson placed two fingers on Ernie's neck and felt Ernie's carotid artery. He turned, looked at Officer Kessler, and shook his head.

DR. ROBERTSON GLANCED up at the emergency room clock. It was 7:03 p.m. on January 31, 1976. Robertson pronounced Ernesto Arturo Miranda dead.

"Hey, Doc," Officer Kessler said, as he entered the room, "I'd like to make a request."

"What would that be, Officer?"

"Could you leave all the tubes and medication in place? It's better to have the detectives see what was done to try to save this man."

NIGHT DETECTIVE ROBERT Nixon arrived at the hospital at 7:30 p.m. and relieved Kessler. Nixon lifted the sheet covering the man's face, hoping to identify him. He had previously worked in the Deuce as an undercover narcotics officer and thought he might recognize the victim. Nixon realized he'd seen the dead man a few years before. He had arrested the man for selling marijuana and asked him to autograph a Miranda Warning card. Nixon identified the deceased as Ernest Miranda. He confirmed the identification by looking at the jailhouse tattoo on Ernie's right hand. There, in the web between the thumb and index finger, were the initials E.M. Nixon further confirmed the dead man's identification by noting an old injury—Ernie was missing the tip of his middle finger on that same hand.

While Ernie's body was moved to the hospital morgue in the basement, Nixon telephoned Scottsdale Police and an Officer Farmer sent a patrol car to the 6800 block of East Diamond Street in Scottsdale. There, Ernie's brother Ruben and Ruben's wife, Mary, were informed of Ernie's death.

RUBEN Miranda remained standing in his doorway after the Scottsdale Police officer left.

At about 12:30 that afternoon Ernie maneuvered Ruben's black and metallic-blue Ford Thunderbird out of the driveway and drove away from Ruben's house. Their last conversation still burned fresh in Ruben's mind. Their brother Benny was getting married that night. Bennie had not invited any of his brothers to the wedding.

Ernie's older brothers had grown up, left home, and joined different branches of the U.S. military. Their careers and tours of duty varied, but each had been successful. Ernie was not considered successful in the eyes of his family.

When Ernie went to prison, only Ruben kept in contact. Ruben would take his two sons, David and Donald, and travel to the state prison at Florence twice a month for visitations. The boys would grow from children into teenagers during the eleven years Ernie spent in Florence. The nephews saw Ernie outside of the prison walls only once, when their grandfather died. Even then, Ernie was flanked by two prison guards at the funeral and at the cemetery. Ernie was allowed to stay only a few hours at the boys' nana's house before being returned to the prison.

Ernie managed to get his first parole in 1972. Ruben and Mary welcomed him into their home. Ernie wanted to go the mall and get some clothes to wear. Ruben and the boys drove Ernie to Los Arcos Mall at Scottsdale and McDowell roads.

"Just drop me off by JC Penney," Ernie said. "I'll find a pay phone and call you when I'm ready to be picked up."

Clothing styles had changed in the previous decade, and Ernie couldn't find any clothing he liked until he went into Chess King. There, the styles had changed very little.

A parole violation for having a gun in the car during a traffic stop put Ernie back in Arizona's Florence prison. Upon his release, he was again taken in by Ruben and Mary.

When the United States Supreme Court overturned Ernie's convictions in the Margaret Fair rape case, and, in the process, created the Miranda Warnings, Ernie attained a kind of notoriety, both in and out of prison. Between stretches in the state pen, Ernie frequented the Deuce in downtown Phoenix, where he gambled and hung out with small-time drug users and undocumented Mexican nationals. Ernie would occasionally autograph Miranda Warning cards, which he sold for a dollar. Ernie liked the attention.

Ernie hadn't said where he was going on the day he was murdered and, as usual, Ruben hadn't asked. Ruben remembered seeing a cloud of cigarette smoke billow from the open driver-side window as the Thunderbird picked up speed and disappeared down the street. Ruben had no idea it would be the last time he would see his brother alive.

HOMICIDE DETECTIVE MARCUS Aurelius arrived at Good Samaritan Hospital at 8:40 p.m. Nixon gave him the Phoenix Fire Department report #76-003545 and Ernie's medical record.

"Scottsdale PD notified the next of kin," Nixon said. "Ruben Miranda should arrive shortly to positively identify the body." Nixon left his completed report, Officer Kessler's report, Ernie's bagged clothing and property items with Detective Aurelius.

"It's kind of odd," Aurelius said.

"What's that?"

"Miranda used a knife when he committed rape, kidnapping, attempted rape, and armed robbery. It's ironic that, ultimately, a knife was used to take his life."

Aurelius read the Fire Department report. Rescue #1 had responded to 233 South 2nd Street, where paramedic personnel found one victim with two stab wounds, one in the chest, and one in the abdomen. The hospital medical records stated the victim had been brought to the Good Sam ER by Universal Ambulance Service. The medical report confirmed the injuries and stated: *Medical therapy was applied, however, there was no response and the victim was pronounced dead at 7:03 p.m.*

Aurelius viewed Ernie's body in the hospital morgue. He noted the injuries sustained and the tubes that had been left in place by the hospital team. R & I Bureau photographer Frank Rodgers responded at Aurelius's request and photographed the body.

Aurelius then inventoried Ernie's clothing as follows: one blue and white print shirt, cut by medical personnel, blood-soaked. One pair of undershorts, one pair of blue trousers, one pair of blue sox, one pair of white loafer shoes, and one blue bandana.

The items removed from Ernie's pockets and body were inventoried as follows: Two yellow metal wrist watches, one set of keys, one pack of cigarettes, one white metal lighter, one black comb, and one brown wallet containing miscellaneous identification papers, a one-dollar bill, and $2.83 in change.

WHEN RUBEN MIRANDA arrived at Good Samaritan Hospital, Detective Aurelius introduced himself and began summarizing the situation. "Mr. Miranda, Ernie was in an altercation at the La Amapola bar at Second Street and Madison. It appears that he was in a fight where he was stabbed twice, once in the abdomen and once in the chest. He died from those injuries."

"I see…" Ruben Miranda dropped his gaze for a moment, then lifted his head and looked into the detective's eyes. "Do you have any suspects?"

"Yes, one Hispanic male with black hair, five foot seven inches, one hundred and fifty pounds. We believe he lives in the Deuce. Do you know of anyone who fits that description who might have wanted to hurt your brother?"

"No," Ruben said. "I didn't even know where he was going. We were together this morning and I loaned him my car just after noon."

"Is your car a black and metallic-blue Thunderbird?"

"Yeah, do you know where it is?"

"It's parked in front of the La Amapola. The keys are in your brother's property bag here." Aurelius lifted the cellophane bag and pointed to the keys. "I can release them to you, along with Ernie's other belongings. But we'll have to keep his clothes as evidence."

"I understand," Ruben said.

Aurelius led Ruben from the nurses' station to the elevator to the hospital morgue in the basement. Hospital personnel had removed the tubes and washed the body. Aurelius pulled back the sheet to reveal Ernie's face.

"It's him," Ruben said. "That's my brother Ernie." Ruben wept.

After a few long moments, Aurelius pulled the sheet over Ernie's face. Ruben left the hospital and Aurelius completed a red tag, used in place of the stereotypical toe tag. Notations on the red tag provided a synopsis of Ernie's death for the medical examiner.

That night Ruben Miranda went to his brother Benny's wedding and notified him that Ernie had been murdered.

EIGHTEEN

PHOENIX POLICE OFFICERS kept people out of the homicide scene by securing the La Amapola Bar's entrance and exit. The witnesses were separated so they would not share information and an officer logged in each officer and detective of every rank who entered the crime scene.

Homicide Lieutenant Nealis arrived and Sergeant Kenner briefed him on the case now known as the Miranda murder. The night detectives who first responded had been relieved by the homicide detectives who took over all aspects of the investigation.

Nealis addressed his men. "Frank Rogers is the only ID Tech we have tonight from R & I Bureau. Right now he's at Good Sam photographing the victim. When he's done there he'll come here and photograph the crime scene. After that he'll have to go to CIB and take photographs and fingerprints of witnesses, investigative leads, and any suspects brought in."

LATER THAT EVENING Detective Quaife left Detective Lash and ID Tech Rogers to finish processing the crime scene around the La Amapola's pool table and stepped over to the bar. Officer Banks introduced him to Adelina Hidalgo. Quaife started asking questions. "I need to get the whole story and you seem to have been in the best position to see what happened. Let me ask you first, do you know the victim?"

"Yeah, he's Ernie Miranda," Adelina said. "He's been coming in for the last few weeks. He usually just has a beer and plays cards."

"Could you tell me what happened earlier today? Before the fight started?"

"Sure, uh, Ernie was playing cards at this end of end of the bar with two other men most of the afternoon."

"Who were the other two men?" Quaife asked.

"One of them was Fernando. I don't know the other man's name. No one called him by his first name, but he was a friend of Fernando's."

"How do know they were friends?"

"I've seen them hanging around together here and at the Nogales Bar. I also heard they live together at the Salt River Hotel."

"Can you describe the man for me? What was Fernando's friend wearing? What was his height and weight, hair and eye color, and anything else you remember about him?"

"He had on a yellow or off-white shirt. Brown pants, I think. He was probably five feet seven, about 130 pounds. His hair was brown, short, and he parted it on the side."

"What happened while they were playing cards?" Quaife asked.

"All three of them started arguing."

"Did you hear what they were arguing about?"

"I heard something about three dollars and then they started fighting. It only lasted a few minutes."

"Were they drunk?"

"The other two men were but Ernie was just sipping his beers and wasn't."

"Then what happened?" Quaife asked.

"I had enough of their arguing and fighting and I took the playing cards away from them. Then I took their beers." Quaife took notes, looked up. "Then what?"

"Ernie went to the restroom and Fernando handed a knife to the other man. Fernando told the man in Spanish, 'Here. You can finish it.'"

"What kind of knife was it? Like a steak knife, or a folding knife?"

"A big folding knife about six or seven inches long."

"What else can you tell me about the knife? Can you describe the handle or was there anything unusual about it?" Quaife asked.

Adelina look toward the ceiling, "Well, I don't know about the handle, but the blade was curved with a hook on the end. That's all I can remember."

"What happened after Fernando gave his friend the knife?"

"Fernando and his girlfriend left the bar and Ernie came out of the restroom."

Quaife wrote some more. "Then what?" "The man with the knife said something to Ernie and it looked like Ernie was trying to take the knife away from him. They were shoving each other and they got over by the pool table, there." Adelina pointed to where a detective and the crime scene tech were working. "And Ernie pushed the man with the knife against the pool table, then the man stabbed Ernie...and Ernie fell on the floor. It was terrible." She lowered her face into one hand.

"I know this is hard for you, but, it's really important. How many times did the man stab Ernie?" Quaife asked.

"I don't know. Maybe two times, I think."

"Then what did the man with the knife do?"

"He walked out of the door and I started to follow him." She wiped her eyes and sniffled. "He still had the knife so I stayed by the doorway."

"What did you see?"

"The man ran down Second Street to the alley behind Madison."

"What did you do then?" Quaife asked.

"I called the fire department and they came. And then an ambulance came and they took Ernie to the hospital."

"Why didn't you call the police?"

"The fire station is just a block away. I thought the firemen could help Ernie. When the cops come everyone just goes to jail."

"I understand." Quaife said. "You're doing very well, Miss Hidalgo. What else can you tell me about the man with the knife? Did he have any scars or marks or tattoos?"

"He was bleeding from a cut across his nose. I think he had a scab there before the fight and Ernie broke it open when he punched him."

"Did you see the knife during that fight?"

"No, Fernando had the knife in his pocket, but no one used it."

"Where are the bottles they were drinking from?" Quaife asked.

Adelina pointed to five Coors beer bottles which she had placed in a cardboard case behind the bar. "They were drinking these beers."

"Did you put the bottles in the box yourself?"

"I did, yes. I had to pour them out into the drain first. But I didn't do that until after the man ran down the street."

"Do you have the ashtray these men were using?"

"Yes, it's here on the bar. I didn't empty it yet."

When the interview concluded an officer drove Adelina Hidalgo to police Headquarters where she waited to be photographed and fingerprinted. At the time it was common to photograph and fingerprint witnesses in order to have their photo on file and exclude the witness's prints from the suspects' prints.

Detective Quaife and Technician Frank Rogers inventoried the evidence collected from the La Amapola crime scene. In addition to photographs, these items consisted of five beer bottles from behind the bar and the cigarette butts from the ashtray on the bar. The investigators also found a small white button and a black and yellow ballpoint pen at the foot of the bar.

They had taken blood swabs from two locations at the crime scene: First, from a blood smear about the size of a human hand, located on the northeast corner area of the pool table itself. Second, from a pool of partially coagulated blood, located on the concrete floor and measuring 30x36 inches. The samples would be submitted for ABO blood typing.

Detectives completed a diagram of the crime scene and all of the items noted were collected, bagged, and marked as evidence.

Officers searched for the murder weapon outside the bar, walking the alley between 2nd and 3rd streets, and between Madison and Jackson streets. Detective Lash would search the alley again during daylight hours on February 1. No one found the weapon.

IN 1974, PHOENIX Police Headquarters moved from the old City Hall to a new four-story concrete structure at 620 W. Washington Street, referred to by officers as "620". The second floor housed the Criminal Investigations Bureau (CIB) where the detectives worked in squads and investigated crimes against persons, such as robbery, assaults, and homicides.

WITHIN AN HOUR after Miranda had been stabbed, Officers Barton and Banks entered the dimly lit Nogales Bar at 29 South 2nd Street, a block north of the La Amapola Bar, and arrested Fernando Rodriguez for the crime. He was held at police headquarters on a charge of Aggravated Assault. Phoenix PD based this charge on information given to the officers. Rodriguez and another man had fought with Miranda and one of the two men had stabbed Miranda. As the night progressed, information developed through witnesses indicating that Rodriguez had facilitated the stabbing of Miranda by allegedly giving the second suspect a knife to commit the crime.

Rodriguez waited in Interview Room One, on the second floor in CIB. He slouched in a wooden chair, his arms resting on a table topped with light blue Formica. The walls were constructed of sheet rock and painted light blue. A 4x6-foot one-way mirror sat in the middle of the wall separating the two interview rooms. The ceiling consisted of white acoustic tile and recessed lights. Rodriguez bent over the table, crossed his arms, and put his head down.

Detective Quaife prepared to interview Rodriguez after gathering as much information as he could from the patrol officers and the evidence at the scene. He intended to find out Rodriguez's involvement with the murder of Ernest Miranda and to determine who his accomplice was. Quaife gathered up a bound notebook, a manila folder filled with completed police reports, and a Styrofoam cup of coffee. Then he and Officer Anthony Bueno stepped into the interview room.

Rodriguez lifted his head and sat up in his chair. He wiped his face with his hands and rubbed his head. He looked groggy to Quaife and he smelled like beer and cigarette smoke. To be sure Rodriguez understood his rights he was advised of his Miranda

Warnings a second time, in Spanish. Officer Bueno did the honors. It was 10:08 p.m. Rodriguez was then told to read the Miranda Warnings card in Spanish. Rodriguez said he understood his rights and that he would voluntarily answer questions. He stated he could read English very well because he had completed the fifth-grade. He agreed to speak to the detective in English.

Quaife noticed Rodriguez's lips were swollen and his bottom lip was cut. His cheeks and forehead had small amounts of blood smeared on them.

Quaife gave Rodriguez the cup of coffee and prepared to take notes. "Mr. Rodriguez," Quaife began, "we have witnesses that have told us you handed a knife to the person that actually did the stabbing of Mr. Miranda."

"Not true. I didn't give a knife to no one."

"When you gave the man the knife you said to him, *Here. You finish it.*"

"I never said that."

"Mr. Rodriguez you told the officers when they found you at the Nogales Bar that you had been in a fight at the La Amapola. You look like you've been in a fight. Your face is swollen, your lip is split, and you told the officer that you had a knife. You do realize that you are in custody for aggravated assault and that you will be charged with the murder of Ernie Miranda."

"Ernie's dead?"

"That's right. He died of the wounds from the knife you gave the other man to use."

Quaife paused. "I need you to tell me what happened today, your side of the story. Start from before you went to the La Amapola, and then what you did at the La Amapola, and after you left. And, tell me who was with you during that time. Do you understand?"

"Yeah, I understand," Rodriguez took a sip from his coffee, pulled it away, licked his swollen lips, set down the coffee and began his story. "I went to the Tivoli at about eleven o'clock this morning."

"Is that the El Tivoli Bar at Second Street and Madison?"

"Yeah."

Quaife wrote. Then he looked up at Rodriguez. "And what did you do there?"

"Drank two or three beers with my girlfriend, Sophia Cortez."

"Then what?" Quaife asked.

"We left there and went to the Nogales and met up with another guy."

"And what was this guy's name?"

"I don't know his name but I recognized him because I seen him around the bars downtown and from working in the fields."

"I need his name." Quaife said.

"I told you, I don't know his name. I know a lot of guys but I don't know their names."

"What happened next?"

"Sophia and me and this guy left to go to the Amapola."

"Amapola, is that the same as La Amapola Bar?"

"Yeah, Amapola."

"What happened there?"

"We saw Sophia's friend, uh, Catalina."

"What's Catalina's last name?"

"I don't know. She's Sophia's friend."

"Okay, then what happened?"

"I played cards all afternoon with some guys."

"Who did you play cards with?" Quaife asked.

"Uh, it was Ernie and the guy I went there with."

"Ernie Miranda?"

"Yeah, Ernie Miranda."

Quaife wrote then looked up. "Okay, what was the other guy's name?"

"I told you, I don't know his name."

"Then what did you call him while you were playing cards all afternoon?"

"I don't know—*Ese*. Yeah, I called him *Ese*."

"I'm supposed to believe that?"

"You can believe what you want. I'm telling you I didn't know his name."

"So why did you call him *Ese*?"

"You know, *Ese*, like *Amigo*, friend."

"So, tell me how did the three of you play cards at the bar?"

"I was on the end seat and Ernie was on the seat next to me. The other guy was standing around the end of the bar."

"What happened next?"

"I passed on a hand and threw my cards on the bar. It was a two-dollar bet."

"Then what happened?"

"That's when Ernie got mad and started punching me for no reason."

"Okay, so Miranda started punching you," Quaife said. "Did you fight back?"

"No, I only put my hands in front of my face. I had to defend myself."

"Let me see your hands."

Rodriguez extended his arms palms up.

"Turn them over."

Quaife noted that Rodriguez's knuckles were not scraped or swollen. "What happened next?"

"We left."

"Who left?"

"I left the Amapola with Sophia and Catalina."

"What about the man you went to the bar with, did he leave too?"

"No he stayed there."

Quaife scribbled in his notebook, then came back to Rodriguez, "Why did you leave?"

"'Cause the fight was over."

"So you left the La Amapola, what happened then?" Quaife asked.

"We got about a block away and I saw the firemen running to the Amapola."

"Then what did you do?"

"I told the girl, Catalina, to go back and see what happened."

"Then what?"

"Then me and Sophia went to the Nogales"

Quaife stopped writing, "What happened to the shirt you were wearing earlier tonight?"

154

"What shirt?"

"I know what you were wearing at the La Amapola, but when the officers found you at the Nogales you were wearing a blue western shirt. Where's the first shirt you had on?"

"Oh, that shirt. There was blood on it from the fight so I borrowed one from a friend at the Nogales."

"Why did you change shirts?" Quaife asked.

"I didn't want to get involved in whatever happened after I left the Amapola."

"What did you think was gonna happen?"

"I don't know what was gonna happen, I left, and whatever happened then I had no part of."

"Well, you are part of it and you need to tell me the name of the other guy that was with you at the La Amapola."

"I told you, I don't know his name. If I knew his name I would tell you."

"This man who did the stabbing, people are telling officers on the street that you have been staying with him, in the same room, for the last three days at the Hayes Hotel."

"Not true. I don't even know where he lives."

"Where do you live?" Quaife asked.

"I mostly stay at Seventh Street and Adams, but right now I'm at the Hayes Hotel."

"What room?"

"Number nine."

"So if I go to your hotel room, will this other man be there?"

"No, why would he be?"

Quaife wrote, then looked up. "What do you know about this man who stabbed Ernie?"

"All I know is he works in the field, for a boss named Diablo."

"What else?"

"Diablo's crew takes the bus from Fifth Street and Madison at six o'clock in the morning. That's really all I know."

Quaife knew Rodriguez was lying. Quaife's experience with suspects told him that Rodriguez was playing cards with his friend and Ernie at the La Amapola Bar. They were probably cheating at cards. The two men were either upset that they got caught cheating by Ernie or that they were being cheated by Ernie. A fight ensued. Ernie was the least intoxicated of the three and the two men lost the fight to him. Ernie went to the restroom. Rodriguez provided the knife for his friend to stab Ernie. When Ernie came out of the restroom the unknown friend stabbed him. Rodriguez may have even seen the stabbing before he and the two other women left the La Amapola.

Quaife didn't have enough to convict Rodriguez on the charges at this point, but there were more witnesses to be interviewed, and he was confident that one of them would tell him the details about Rodriguez's involvement. After two hours and twenty minutes the interview with Fernando Zamura Rodriguez ended.

Quaife directed Officer Barton to seize all of Rodriguez's clothing except his underwear. Barton collected a pair of light blue pants with blood spots; a dark blue, long sleeve western shirt, and a pair of brown shoes. Quaife then impounded the clothing as evidence and submitted the paperwork for the blood to be analyzed by the lab. Rodriguez was booked into Maricopa County jail for the murder of Ernest Miranda.

NINETEEN

DETECTIVE QUAIFE CONTACTED Sergeant Malody of the downtown walking beat around 12:30 a.m. and gave him the description of the man wanted for stabbing Ernest Miranda. Quaife told Malody that the man might be hiding out in room number nine of the Hayes Hotel. Sergeant Malody instructed Officers Jere Miller and George Maxwell to meet him at the Hayes Hotel. They searched for the suspect and any evidence that might link him to the murder of Miranda. Miller and Maxwell found no evidence and no suspect at the Hayes Hotel.

There were a dozen more hotels in the Deuce. Malody had his officers split up in order to contact the managers of each one and ask if they had seen anyone fitting the suspect's description. Malody made contact at hotels on Washington and 3rd Streets.

1:00 a.m. on February 1, 1976, Sergeant Malody interviewed the night clerk at the Salt River Hotel at 233 E. Washington. The clerk told Malody about a man there that fit the suspect's description: Mexican male, twenty-three years old, five feet seven, 130 to 150 lbs., dark brown hair combed back. The clerk said there were three men registered to the room.

Malody had word sent to Officers Miller and Maxwell and they met him in the hotel lobby. The three officers went to the room. The door was slightly ajar. They knocked, then entered the room and found two men sleeping in different beds. An elderly white male lay asleep on a bed set against the west wall of the room. In the bed against the north wall, the officers observed a Mexican male who roughly fit the description of the suspect. When they woke this man they discovered he had a cut on the left side of the bridge of his nose. He identified himself as Eseziquel Moreno, a Mexican national. They took him into custody at 1:30 a.m. for the murder of Ernest Miranda.

ROUGHLY THE SAME time, Detective Quaife was questioning Sophia Cortez in Interview Room Two at police headquarters. He began by asking the witness, "Miss Cortez what is your relationship with Fernando Rodriguez?

"Fernando is my boyfriend."

"And can you tell me about the fight that occurred with your boyfriend and Ernie Miranda earlier tonight at the La Amapola Bar?"

"Yeah, me and Fernando were at the La Amapola and Fernando got into an argument with Ernie."

"What was the argument about?"

"I don't know. Ernie started the fight with Fernando and some other guy who was with us."

"What was the other guy's name?"

"I don't know."

"Okay, so you're saying the other guy is a friend of Fernando's but you don't know his name."

"No. He's Fernando's friend, not mine."

"Okay, so Ernie started the fight. Did Fernando fight back?"

"No. And after the fight I told him we should leave."

"What happened next?" Quaife asked.

"Me and Fernando left."

"Then what happened?"

"A little while later the firemen went to the La Amapola."

"And what did you do?"

"I told Catalina to go back and tell Angelina that we were not going to hide because we got nothing to hide about."

"Okay, back up a minute. Who is Catalina?"

"Catalina Gomez, she's my friend."

"And she was with you at the La Amapola."

"Yeah."

"And who is Angelina?"

"Angelina Hidalgo, she's my half-sister." Sophia leaned in and shook her fist. "She better not say that Fernando and me got anything to do about the guy stabbing Ernie."

"Easy," Quaife said as he sat back and put his hands up in surrender position. "No one is accusing you of anything."

"Well if they do…"

"Miss Cortez," Quaife said calmly, "why do you think Ernie was stabbed?"

"'Cause you said he was."

"No, I didn't say Ernie was stabbed. Why do you think Ernie was stabbed?"

"The firemen came and the ambulance after that, and they took Ernie to the hospital. It had to be a stabbing."

"Okay, let's talk a little slower and quieter, all right? Can you do that for me?" Quaife asked.

"I'm sorry. I can. I'm just upset that we're being involved with something we had nothing to do with."

"Miss Cortez," Quaife said. "I think you, Fernando, and Catalina were all inside the La Amapola when the stabbing happened."

"No, that's not true. We left and went to The Nogales. And I told Fernando he better change his shirt with blood on it for a different one so no one thinks we were involved. Then he went to the restroom and he came out with a different shirt."

"Who gave Fernando the other shirt?"

"I don't know. All I know is the cops came into the bar and arrested Fernando."

"I see there are drops of blood on your shirt. How did they get there?" Quaife asked.

Sophia sat back in her chair, grabbed her blouse at her waist, pulled it away from her and scoured it with her eyes. "I don't know, must be Fernando's blood from when we walked to the Nogales."

"I think you saw more than what you're saying and you need to tell me about it."

"No, we're not involved," Sophia crossed her arms and stared at the table. "I don't know what Angelina told you. That's all I remember and that's all I'm saying."

Quaife ended the interview and had Sophia Cortez photographed and fingerprinted before he let her go.

OFFICERS MILLER AND Maxwell were waiting in the hallway outside of the interview rooms when Detective Quaife came back from escorting Sophia Cortez to the R & I Bureau.

"Sergeant Malody said you would want to interview the man we found at the Salt River Hotel." Miller said.

"Yes, what his name?"

"Eseziquel Moreno. Here's a 36 card on him," Maxwell said.

"What'd you tell him? You read him his rights or anything?" Quaife asked.

"No, nothing. We had Officer Hernandez tell him in Spanish that a detective wanted to talk to him and Hernandez helped us with the 36 card 'cause Moreno says he doesn't speak any English," Miller said.

"Okay, fine. Where is he?"

"Interview Room Two, Hernandez is in there with him."

Quaife entered Interview Room Two with a manila folder and a note pad in his hand. Officer Tommy Hernandez waited just inside the door. Quaife stood for a moment, looking at Moreno, who sat in a chair on the far side of the table. Moreno had a noticeable injury to the bridge of his nose. The injury was partially scabbed over as if it were a week old and had recently been reopened. Quaife also observed a cut on the third finger of Moreno's right hand. The cut appeared to be several days old. Quaife could smell stale beer on Moreno's breath and cigarette smoke on his clothes. Quaife and Officer Hernandez took a seat at the table and began interviewing Moreno.

Hernandez read the Miranda Warnings in Spanish to Moreno at 2:10 a.m. Moreno replied in Spanish that he understood his rights and would answer questions. He said he had no need for an attorney because he had done nothing wrong. He seemed confident and wanted to know why the police wanted to talk to him.

Detective Quaife asked questions in English. Officer Hernandez translated while Quaife made notes.

"Where are you currently living?" Quaife asked.

"The Salt River Hotel." Moreno said.

"Where were you earlier today?"

"At my hotel most of the day."

"Did you leave your hotel anytime today?"

"I went to the Nogales."

Quaife wrote, then looked up at Moreno. "The Nogales Bar?"

"Yes."

"Who were you with at the Nogales?" Quaife waited for the translated response.

"I was alone. In the restaurant part of the bar"

"What time were you there?"

"I would say between six and seven o'clock."

"What did you eat?"

"I ordered chicken."

"Then what did you do?"

"I went to my room about a half hour later."

"Did you go to any other bars?"

"No. I don't like to drink in the downtown bars."

"You smell like you've been drinking. Where did you drink?" Quaife asked.

"I had a beer in my room with some guys at the hotel."

"How did you cut your nose?"

Moreno touched his nose, "I fell on the steps getting on the work bus a few days ago. Hit my nose on the step."

The translation was interrupting the normal flow of the interrogation and Quaife became frustrated that he wasn't extracting the information needed. He was getting mixed signals from Moreno's posture and the lapse in time in his responses. He continued. "Let me see your hands."

Moreno held out his hands palm down, then turned them palms up.

"How did you cut your finger?"

"I was working in the fields and cut it with a knife."

"What kind of knife?" Quaife asked.

"It was a lettuce field, I had a lettuce knife."

Quaife showed Moreno a black and white photograph of the other suspect, Fernando Rodriguez. "Do you know this man?"

"I don't know him." Moreno said.

Quaife needed more information and evidence to tie Moreno to the murder of Miranda. He would need a witness to put him at the scene.

It was approaching 3:00 a.m. and the witnesses were no longer at the station. Moreno claimed to have been at the Nogales Bar, not at the La Amapola. He was staying at a Deuce hotel and had a job. Quaife would have Moreno photographed and fingerprinted and show a photographic lineup to the witnesses in the morning. If Moreno was identified as the suspect who did the stabbing, Quaife would have him arrested and booked into jail for the murder of Ernest Miranda.

Moreno voluntarily submitted to being photographed and fingerprinted. Officers Miller and Maxwell returned Moreno to the Salt River Hotel.

QUAIFE BRIEFED HIS sergeant, who in turn made a blue-book entry to be read in shift briefings. Dispatchers broadcasted the information available, stating that the second suspect was still on the loose. The case status was changed from open to "Cleared by Arrest" because of the arrest of one of the suspects—Fernando Rodriguez. The case would be closed after the second suspect was apprehended.

WHEN MIRANDA WAS killed, Fernando Rodriguez had been on probation for sales of narcotic drugs. He had pled guilty to that charge back on June 29, 1973. Rodriguez's involvement in the Miranda murder brought attention to the fact that he was drinking and associating with known convicted felons. This violated his probation. Although Rodriguez was never tried for the murder of Ernest Miranda, he was sentenced to five to seven years in the Arizona State Prison system for the probation violations.

FEBRUARY 1, 1976, the day after Ernest Miranda's murder, walking beat officers located witness Angelina Hidalgo and showed her several 2x3-inch photographs, including a photograph of Esequelle Moreno. She identified Esequelle Moreno as the man who delivered the alleged fatal knife wounds to Ernest Miranda. Detectives attempted to locate Moreno. All sources led them to believe that the suspect had already fled to his native Mexico.

Detective Quaife had a warrant sworn out for the arrest of Esequelle Moreno for first degree murder, a class 1 felony, in the death of Ernest A. Miranda.

The suspect was never apprehended.

EPILOGUE

THE SUPREME COURT'S 1966 ruling on Miranda was again
the subject of legislation in the United States Congress in 1968. The
U.S. Congress attempted to undo the effect of the Miranda Decision
by passing a law, 18 U.S.C. Â§3501, stating that in a federal trial a
confession could be admitted against a criminal defendant if the
judge found it to have been "voluntary," even if "Miranda
Warnings" had not been given.

In 1999, the U.S. Court of Appeals for the Fourth Circuit ruled,
in reference to the Miranda Decision, that the law passed by
Congress in 1968, 18 U.S.C. Â§3501, having been enacted later than
the Miranda Decision, overruled it. In the 7-to-2 decision in
Dickerson v. U.S., 530 U.S. 428 (2000), the high court upheld the
Miranda Decision by reversing the Fourth Circuit's judgment and
ruling that the holding in the Miranda Decision was a matter of
constitutional law and therefore higher than any legislation Congress
passed.

The Supreme Court again reaffirmed this, one of the most
important decisions of the 20th century—the Miranda Decision—on
June 29, 2000, upholding the 1966 Miranda vs. Arizona ruling that
assures the right against self-incrimination and the right to an
attorney.

REFERENCES

Chapter ONE: The Kidnap, Rape and Robbery
Department Report #63-08380
Officer John A. Page Jr. #855 - 03-03-1961, resigned, 09-17-1965
Night Detectives: Kyle W. Gourdoux #522 - 03-09-1959, retired, 12-31-1979
Darwin "Don" Davis #524 - 03-09-1959, resigned, 01-25-1966
Edwin W. Smith, #581 - 05-25-1959, deceased, 05-05-1968
Court Documentation: The Arizona Republic and the Phoenix Gazette
Interview of Detective Carroll F. Cooley #413 - 04-28-1958, retired captain 12-31-1978

Chapter TWO: Patrol and Initial Detective Response
Department Report #63-08380
Officer John A. Page Jr. #855 - 03-03-1961, resigned, 09-17-1965
Night Detectives: W. Gourdoux #522 - 03-09-1959, retired, 12-31-1979
Darwin "Don" Davis #524 - 03-09-1959, resigned, 01-25-1966
Assaults Detective Sergeant Seymour S. Nealis #193 - 12-01-1952, retired lieutenant, 05-18-1979
Day shift Assaults Detectives: Wilfred "Bill" M. Young #182 - 12-01-1952, retired, 12-31-1978, deceased
Edwin W. Smith, #581 - 05-25-1959, deceased, 05-05-1968
Bobby G. Manning #493 - 02-09-1959, resigned, 08-26-1966
Arthur R. Monroe Jr. #859 - 06-16-1961, retired, 11-30-1981

Chapter THREE: Confirming the Victim's Story
Department Report #63-08380
Detective Sergeant Seymour S. Nealis #193 - 12-01-1952, retired lieutenant05-18-1979
Det. Richard "Dick" R. Golden #751 - 06-27-1960, resigned, 06-02-1967
Interview of Detective Carroll F. Cooley #413 - 04-28-1958, retired captain, 12-31-1978

Chapter FOUR: Victim Barbara Sue McDaniel
Department Report #62-40126
Officer Thomas R. Ezell #212 - 12-01-1952, retired, 12-31-1973

Chapter FIVE: Crimes Against Persons November 1962
Related Police Reports:
62-40127 – 62-39256 – 62-38337 – 62-37957 – 62-37822 – 62-37502 – 62-31928 – 62-26239 – 62-40126
Detectives: Robert Kornegay #479 - 11-17-1958, retired assistant chief,

REFERENCES

1999, deceased 2001
Perko, Randall #989 - 01-07-1963, resigned, 02-03-1966
Larry Loren Debus #520, 02-09-1959, resigned, 08-19-1964
Gilbert W. Brady Jr.#559 - 04-13-1959, retired, 07-30-1982
Bobby G. Manning #493 - 02-09-1959, resigned, 08-26-1966
Glenn W. Martin #70 - Hired prior to 1952, retired 05-28-1964
Interview of Officer R. Brian Kornegay #5132 - 03-20-1989, to Present
(son of Robert Kornegay #479)

Chapter SIX: The Barns Parking Lot
Department Report #63-07180
Officers: W.O. Simmons #596 - 06-22-1959, resigned, 07-31-1964
Joe Q. Garcia #539 - 04-01-1959, retired, 08-11-1976
Detectives: Donald M. Procunier #508 - 02-09-1959, resigned, 08-31-1966
Richard O. Rimer #414 - 04-28-1958, resigned, 07-19-1966

Chapter SEVEN: The Polygraph
Department Report #63-08380
Detective Carroll F. Cooley #413 - 04-28-1958, retired captain 12-31-1978
Phoenix Police Department's Polygraph Examiner Sergeant Earl Moore
#139 - 2-27-1947, retired, 9-19-1969
Policewoman Edna Hoffman-Hurt #469 - 08-11-1958, retired, 08-11-1978
Interview of Current Phoenix Police Department's Polygraph Examiner
Billy Wingo A4567 - 01-05-2004 to present

Chapter EIGHT: A Break in the Case
Department Report #63-08380
David A. Anderson #766 - 06-27-1960, retired, 07-30-1983
Detective Wilfred "Bill" M. Young #182, 12-01-1952, retired, 12-31-1978,
deceased
Interview of Detective: Carroll F. Cooley #413 - 04-28-1958, retired
captain, 12-31-1978

Chapter NINE: Arresting Officer Carroll Cooley
Department report #63-08380
The Arizona Republic and the Phoenix Gazette
Detectives: Wilfred "Bill" M. Young #182 - 12-01-1952, retired, 12-31-
1978, deceased
Joe Q. Garcia #539 - 04-01-1959, retired, 08-11-1976
Ernest Tautimes #997 - 03-01-1963, resigned, 10-15-1965
Interview of Detective Carroll F. Cooley #413 - 04-28-1958, retired

REFERENCES

captain, 12-31-1978

Chapter TEN: The Trails of Ernest Miranda
Judge Barry G. Silverman - U.S. Court of Appeals for the Ninth Circuit
Former Maricopa County Superior Court judge.
Silverman, Barry G. "Remembering Miranda: 40 years after the landmark decision" - Phoenix Magazine, June 2006, 108-115
Stuart, Gary L. *Miranda: the story of America's right to remain silent.* Tucson: University of Arizona Press, 2004. Print
Decision and Rationale, source: ©2005 Pearson Education, Inc., publishing as Pearson Prentice Hall.
1966 Transcript of Miranda v. Arizona-Sam Mahoney Jan 16, 2013
"Explore the History of Lewis and Roca" – see section: "1966 – Miranda v. Arizona" - Lewis & Roca. Archived from the original on 2008-05-14. Retrieved 2011-08-24. Accessed July 25, 2013 1:10PM
Accessed July 25, 2013, 1:14PM
The Arizona Republic and the Phoenix Gazette

Chapter ELEVEN: Business as Usual
Departmental Report #63-29077
Arizona Republic and the Phoenix Gazette
Detective Sergeant Seymour S. Nealis #193 - 12-01-1952, retired lieutenant05-18-1979
Detectives: Ralph Jenson Cluff #516 - 02-09-1959, retired, 04-30-1979
Richard "Dick" B. Murphey #380, 12-02-1957, retired, Commander 03-31-1982, 04-14-2015, deceased
Scott R. Chestnut #360 - 07-01-1957, resigned, 06-15-1967
Donald M. Procunier #508 - 02-29-1959, resigned, 08-31-1966
Officers: James P. Adams #484 - 02-09-1959, retired, 12-31-1980
Reuben L. Berry#557 - 04-13-1959, retired, 06-29-1979
William E. MacGill #144 - 02-24-1947, retired, 10-31-1969

Chapter TWELVE: Center City Motel Robberies
Departmental Report #63-29531
The Arizona Republic and the Phoenix Gazette
Lieutenant George Sanders #149 - 02-27-47, retired, 01-19-1973
Sergeant Samual B. Howe #375 - 10-01-57, retired, 04-30-1981
Interview of retired Lieutenant Blaine Thompson #271 - 05-09-55, retired lieutenant, 03-01-1982, deceased 10-01-2014
Desk Sergeant Albert T. Edens #166 - 03-15-52, retired
Detective David L. Haynes #643 - 10-12-1959, retired, 1987

REFERENCES

Interview of Detective Carroll F. Cooley #413 - 04-28-1958, retired rank of captain, 12-31-1978
Officer Reuben L. Berry#557 04-13-1959, retired, 06-29-1979
W.O. Simmons #596 - 06-22-1959, resigned 07-31-1964
Joe Q. Garcia #539 - 04-01-1959, retired, 08-11-1976
Reserve Officer Sam Leabo #R22 - 06-03-62 - was Chief of Reserves 1968-1975, October 2013, deceased

Chapter THIRTEEN: A Meeting with the Chief
Chief Charlie P. Thomas #32 - 01-03-1942, retired 12-31-1963, deceased 1989
Sergeant Seymour S. Nealis #193 - 12-01-1952, retired lieut. 05-18-1979
Interview of Detective Carroll F. Cooley #413 - 04-28-1958, retired captain, 12-31-1978
Retired Captain T.R. Lefty Mofford - retired prior to 1952
Interview:
Retired Assistant Chief Michael McCort #3572 - 04-30-1979, retired assistant chief 06-30-2008 - Gave the eulogy at Chief Thomas funeral.
Mark D. McCort #572 - 05-25-1959, retired rank of lieutenant 07-27-1981 – deceased. Father of Michael McCort who served under Chief Thomas.
Interview of Chief Thomas' Confidant Robert Settembre #3633 - 06-25-1979 retired lieutenant 12-31-2014, Reserve #R1293 –
State of Arizona House of Representatives Forty-Fifth Legislature Second Regular Session 2002 - HR 2007

Chapter FOURTEEN: The Supreme Court's Cluster
Judge Barry G. Silverman - U.S. Court of Appeals for the Ninth Circuit Former Maricopa County Superior Court judge.
Silverman, Barry G. "Remembering Miranda: 40 years after the landmark decision" - Phoenix Magazine, June 2006, 108-115
Stuart, Gary L. *Miranda: the story of America's right to remain silent.* Tucson: The University of Arizona Press, 2004. Print
Decision and Rationale, source: ©2005 Pearson Education, Inc., publishing as Pearson Prentice Hall.
1966 Transcript of Miranda v. Arizona - Sam Mahoney Jan 16, 2013
"Explore the History of Lewis and Roca" – see section: "1966 – Miranda v. Arizona" Lewis & Roca. Archived from the original on 2008-05-14. Retrieved 2011-08-24. Accessed July 25, 2013, 1:10PM
Accessed July 25, 2013, 1:14PM
The Arizona Republic and the Phoenix Gazette

REFERENCES

Chapter FIFTEEN: Twila Hoffman
Departmental report #76 – 011123
Arizona Republic and the Phoenix Gazette
Interview of Detective: Carroll F. Cooley #413 - 04-28-1958, retired rank of captain, 12-31-1978

Chapter SIXTEEN: The La Amapola Bar
Departmental report #76 – 011123
The Arizona Republic and the Phoenix Gazette

Chapter SEVENTEEN: Miranda's Death
Departmental report #76 – 011123
The Arizona Republic and the Phoenix Gazette
Sergeant Larry A. Risner #1323 - 10-04-1965, retired, 03-31-1986
Officers: Gary W. Barton #2530 - 04-09-1973, retired, 08-31-1993
John A. Williams #1384 - 08-22-1966, retired, 10-24-1995
Robert E. Lee #3036 - 11-17-1975, resigned, 07-17-1982.
Gordon P. Costa #2889 - 05-19-1975, retired, 05-22-1996
George J. Banks #1761 - 04-07-1969, resigned, 06-30-1973, rehired 11-05-1973, resigned 08-11-1969
Warren L. Friederman Jr. #2516 - 03-12-1973, retired, 01-18-1994
Kenneth E. Kessler #2632 - 10-08-1973, resigned, 12-07-1976
Sergeant Glenn Kenner #915 - 04-02-1962, retired 07-25-1990
Night Detectives:
Calvin E. Lash Jr. #1658 - 08-19-1968, retired, 03-29-1991
Robert E. Nixon #2104 - 05-10-1971, retired, 05-28-1991
Homicide Detective:
Ronald G. Quaife #1111 - 01-06-1964, retired, 01-31-1984
G. Marcus Aurelius Jr. #1653 - 07-22-1968, retired captain 07-27-1999
R & I Bureau Photographer, Identification Officer, Frank Rodgers A504 - 10-29-1966, retired 13-29-2001
Interviews of Detectives:
Calvin E. Lash Jr. #1658 - 08-19-1968, retired, 03-29-1991
G. Marcus Aurelius Jr. #1653 - 07-22-1968, retired captain 07-27-1999
David R. Miranda #3909 - 12-01-1980, retired, 05-27-201, Reserve #R1140, Son of Reuben Miranda, Nephew to Ernie Miranda

Chapter EIGHTEEN and NINETEEN:
The Investigation of Miranda's Death
Departmental Report #76 – 011123
The Arizona Republic and the Phoenix Gazette

REFERENCES

Lieutenant Seymour S. Nealis #193 - 12-01-1952, retired, 05-18-1979
Sergeant Francis Malody #1386 - 08-22-1966, retired lieutenant, 09-16-1988
Homicide Sergeant Glenn Kenner #915 - 04-02-1962, retired 07-25-1990
Night Detectives:
Calvin E. Lash Jr. #1658 - 08-19-1968, retired, 03-29-1991
Homicide Detective:
Ronald G. Quaife #1111 - 01-06-1964, retired, 01-31-1984
G. Marcus Aurelius Jr. #1653 - 07-22-1968, retired captain 07-27-1999
Officer Jere A. Miller #1611 - 03-25-1968, resigned, 03-27-1981
Officer George F. Maxwell #2520 - 03-26-1973, retired, 07-06-2006
Officer Anthony R. Bueno #2311 - 05-22-1972, retired, 07-14-2006, Reserve #R0854
R & I Bureau Photographer, Identification Tech, Frank Rodgers A504 - 10-29-1966, retired 13-29-2001
Joseph R Farmer #534 - 03-09-1959, retired rank of Lieutenant
Cooley, Carroll F. with Farmer, Joseph R. "The Inside Story of Miranda" Arizona Peace Office Standard and Training Board, 1980, 70-81.
Interviews of Detectives:
Carroll F. Cooley #413 - 04-28-1958, retired captain 12-31-1978
Calvin E. Lash Jr. #1658 - 08-19-1968, retired, 03-29-1991
G. Marcus Aurelius Jr. #1653 - 07-22-1968, retired captain 07-27-1999
David R. Miranda #3909 - 12-01-1980, retired, 05-27-201, Reserve #R1140 - Son of Reuben Miranda, Nephew to Ernie Miranda
Interviews of Cold Case Detectives:
Mark Amistead #4592 - 07-07-1986 to Present
Jesus Antonio F. Jimenez #4785 - 05-18-1987 to Present

ACKNOWLEDGEMENTS

Organizations:

Phoenix Police Department - Phoenix Police Chief Joseph Yahner

Phoenix Police Museum - Curator Michael Nikolin Retired Phoenix Lieutenant, Dennis Garrett retired Police Chief, James Pina retired Assistant Police Chief, Carroll Cooley retired Captain, Robert Demlong retired Commander, Rob Settembre retired Lieutenant, Steve Proctor retired Sergeant, Wayne Bensfield retired Sergeant, Don Steinmetz retired Sergeant, Leo Speliopoulos retired Detective, Sal Garcia retired Detective, Ed Reynolds retired Detective, Earl Fisher retired Detective, Dick Todd retired Detective, Walt Taggert retired Detective, Tom Schmeltz retired Officer, Gary Bishop retired Officer, Russ Pedraza retired Police Assistant, and Museum Docent Sue Bell, C.P.A. Cheri Craig and former Museum Historian Cathy Bell.

Phoenix Police Lieutenant Chris Moore, EL Mirage Lieutenant Laura Liuzzo, Phoenix Police Sergeant Charmane Osborn, Sergeant Mark Doty, Detective Robert Sitek, Officer Frank Marino, Officer Jennifer Eastman, Officer Vince Cole, Volunteer Linda Schwall, and "The Historian" Newsletter Editor Scott Bagger.

Sisters in Crime Desert Sleuths Chapter President, Isabella Maldonado

Fraternal Order of Police (FOP) Phoenix Lodge #2
Lou Manganiello Retired Phoenix Police Officer
Jim Mann Executive Director at Fraternal Order of Police, Arizona Labor Council

Phoenix Police Sergeants and Lieutenants Association (PPSLA)

President Sean Mattson, Phoenix Police Sergeant

Phoenix Law Enforcement Association (PLEA)

President Joe R. Clure, Phoenix Police Officer
Former PLEA President Jake Jacobson, Retired Phoenix Police Officer

Association of Retired Phoenix Officers (ARPO) President John Augustyn, Retired Phoenix Police Lieutenant

International Police Association (IPA) Region #25 President Gus Bart and Third Vice President Larry Amabile Retired Phoenix Police Sergeant.

Arizona Historical Society - President Leonard Marcisz

100 Club of Arizona - Executive Director Sharon Knutson-Felix

CL Printing Phoenix, Arizona - Thom Meeker

ACKNOWLEDGEMENTS

Phoenix Police Employees who gave great support:
Senior Sergeant Vernon Busby, Sergeant Charles Gwinn retired, Sergeant William Wren retired, Sergeant John Ramsey retired, Sergeant Scott Masino retired, Detective Robert Sitek, Detective Rico Fragoso retired, Detective Danny Webb retired, Admin I, Armando Serrata, and Secretary III, Randi Stratos.

Those who gave us guidance:
Deborah J Ledford, past-president of the Sisters in Crime Desert Sleuths Chapter, is an award-winning author, master editor and mentor.

Kästle Olson took great care of the website design and the book cover.

Lisa Anderson is an excellent freelance editor from Tucson.

Megan D. Scott, Esq. - Volunteer Legal Assistance for Artists.

Honorable Judge Barry Silverman United States Courts of the 9th Circuit.

We thank you all.

AUTHOR BIOGRAPHIES

Following several years as a patrol officer, **TIMOTHY W. MOORE** has been a detective for nearly two and half decades, working a wide range of detective assignments. He began in the Property Crimes Bureau then Airport Investigations Unit and Property Management Bureau. He was assigned the Family Investigations Bureau—Assaults Unit, Violent Crimes Bureau—Homicide Detail, before an appointment as a Court Liaison to the Maricopa County Attorney's Office. He was then selected to work in the Laboratory Services Bureau, was the Administrative Detective in the Reserve Division and is currently assigned to the Violent Crimes Bureau's—Crime Gun Intelligence Squad. Moore has been married to his wife, Laurie, for 29 years and they have two grown daughters Jessa and Jarah.

CLARK LOHR has written and published two novels, *Devil's Kitchen* and *The Devil on Eighty-Five*. He holds degrees in Writing, Literature and English from the University of Arizona and is an accomplished professional still photographer. He is a Vietnam vet and a member of Veterans for Peace and the Desert Sleuths Chapter of Sister's in Crime. He lives and writes in Tucson, Arizona.

Made in the USA
Charleston, SC
12 September 2016